'When the comparatively small island of Tasmania becomes more densely populated, and its primitive forests are intersected with roads from the eastern to the western coast, the numbers of this singular animal will speedily diminish, extermination will have its full sway, and it will then, like the Wolf in England and Scotland, be recorded as an animal of the past...'

John Gould, Naturalist, 1863

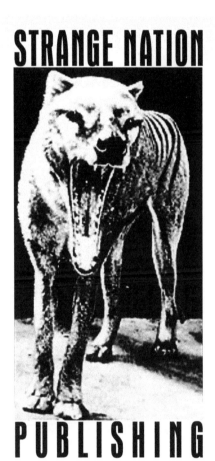

STRANGE NATION

PUBLISHING

THE
TASMANIAN
TIGER

EXTINCT OR EXTANT?

FOREWORD by Dr KARL SHUKER

EDITED by REBECCA LANG

Cover design by Tim Hartridge.

Main image copyright Queen Victoria Museum.

Book layout by Rebecca Lang

ISBN: 978 0 646 92634 6

First Edition: September 2014

For information contact; www.australian-tasmanian-tiger.com

CONTENTS

A 1935 postcard combining images of a captive Thylacine with Tasmania's scenic Cradle Mountain, in the north-west of the island, in the background. *Courtesy of the Queen Victoria Museum.*

FOREWORD

Is the Thylacine truly extinct, or merely evanescent?

The Thylacine (aka zebra wolf, Tasmanian wolf, or Tasmanian tiger) is often drily referred to as the world's most common extinct animal – and for good reason. Even though the last confirmed specimen, poor lonely Benjamin, famously died in 1936 in Hobart Zoo, in the decades that have followed this iconic species has quite literally refused to lay down and die.

Instead, report after report, sighting after sighting, of large canine-like beasts with striped backs, stiff tails, and gaping jaws briefly but memorably encountered in the wilds of Tasmania has continued to hit the media and cryptozoological headlines.

So is the Thylacine truly extinct, or merely evanescent? Has it genuinely been extirpated, or is it simply very elusive? Year after year, diligent privately-funded investigators trek through this Australian island state's often-remote bush country in search of tangible evidence to confirm this tantalising mammal's survival, to collect further anecdotal evidence as the basis for future quests, and – surely the Holy Grail for all cryptozoologists – to experience a first-hand, camera-equipped encounter with the largest yet most mysterious of all modern-day carnivorous marsupials.

During the course of its official post-extinction period, the Thylacine has been the subject of many books, but this present volume is very special, because, uniquely, it assimilates the personal experiences of a number of very different but all equally determined, highly experienced Tasmanian Tiger seekers and chroniclers. Some have pursued it in libraries and online data sources via bibliographical research, others in its native domain via field research, and all have added immeasurably to the fund of information on record concerning this truly spectacular species.

Nor have they collectively confined their attention and scope to Tasmania during their searches. For only a few millennia ago, the Thylacine was also very much alive in mainland Australia, and even in New Guinea too, but by the time that BC had been replaced by AD in the history of humanity, the Thylacine had vanished from both of these regions – hadn't it?

Just as in Tasmania, there is a sizeable archive of cryptozoological material on file testifying to the potential present-day existence of mainland and Papuan Thylacines.

In the former case, if the creatures being sighted are truly Tasmanian Tigers then they could be canny native survivors, or, if an alternative, highly intriguing theory proposed by some investigators is to taken seriously, they may actually be naturalised descendants of Tasmanian specimens introduced and freed on the mainland many decades ago.

As for New Guinea reports: the alleged presence in Irian Jaya (Indonesian New Guinea) of a striped canine mystery beast known as the *dobsegna* that bears a striking resemblance to the Thylacine, if local descriptions are to be believed, is ample reason to retain hope that there may be more than just morphological comparability behind these accounts.

And what about the most exciting, extraordinary possibility of all? Even if the Thylacine is never rediscovered in the wild, could it instead be resurrected in the laboratory?

What may once have sounded like sensationalised science fiction is now very much within the boundaries of sober sciençe fact, thanks to ever-advancing genetic techniques that have already succeeded in producing viable cloned specimens of several other animal species. Why not the Thylacine too one day? A famous conservation slogan once warned that extinction is forever, but perhaps the time is not too far off when only the slogan will be demised, not its subjects.

And so, without further ado, I eagerly invite you to peruse and enthuse each and every one of the thought-provoking contributions within this extremely compelling and thoroughly fascinating compendium of contemporary Thylacine field and armchair research.

And I guarantee that if you don't come away from them with a much more emphatic belief in the possible persistence of Tasmania's most famous four-legged personification than you harboured before you began reading them, then I can only assume that your spirit of hopeful optimism must surely be as deceased as the TasmanianTiger is...or isn't!

Dr Karl P.N. Shuker, December 2013

A replica Tasmanian Tiger skull poised in front of car manufacturer Toyota's logo. Toyota Australia generously supplied 4WDs for several Tasmanian expeditions during 2013-2014. *Courtesy of Rebecca Lang.*

INTRODUCTION

There is passionate debate about the Thylacine's continued existence

The last Thylacine in captivity died on September 7, 1936, ironically just two weeks shy of the species receiving protection status. In 1986, 50 years later, it would be declared extinct. By international standards it no longer exists, and is just another marsupial ghost haunting the Australian landscape following European settlement.

While Benjamin is often symbolically referred to as 'The Last Thylacine', in all likelihood the species persisted in the Tasmanian wilderness well into the 1930s, possibly until the 1950s. In 1980 then-Tasmanian Parks and Wildlife officer Steven Smith conducted a detailed study of sightings between 1934 and 1980, concluding of the 320 sightings, just under half could be considered good, if inconclusive.

Judging by the thousands of sightings logged by government departments and private research groups since that time, however, it may still roam remote parts of Tasmania.

Interestingly, reports also hail from unlikely mainland locations including corners of south-west Victoria and south-west Western Australia, and from as far afield as NSW and Queensland. Up north and across the Arafura Sea, indigenous people report sightings of a strange striped dog-like creature, prompting speculation that the Thylacine still dwells in the rainforests and highlands of Irian Jaya, where new species are still being discovered.

So is it or isn't it still out there?

Like many the world over, I've always been intrigued by the idea that out there, somewhere, the Thylacine still prowls the far reaches of Australia's vast southern wilderness, slipping between light and shadow, camouflaged amid dappled vegetation thanks to its distinctive dark stripes and brackish fur.

I've been collecting and investigating reports of alleged Thylacines on and off for many years on both the mainland and in Tasmania – most recently during a series of expeditions staged during 2013-2014, generously sponsored by Toyota Australia.

One of the very first reports I collected was back in 2000 and took place in Western Australia. I was working as a journalist at the time when a woman contacted me about her 1970s sighting. Her family had been crossing the Nullarbor Plain when they saw not one but several Thylacines (a family?) wander past their car during a rest break. The sighting occurred several years *after* the 1966 discovery of a remarkably 'fresh' looking carcass discovered in a cave nearby, the so-called 'Nullarbor Thylacine' discussed in detail in Chapter 8.

My mind boggled at the prospect of Thylacines outside of Tasmania. I knew so little about the animals at that stage it seemed highly improbable, if not impossible. And yet the deeper I have delved into the subject, the more frequently such mainland reports have cropped up. Could it be that the Thylacine, which also once roamed the length and breadth of Australia and Irian Jaya/Papua New Guinea, has held some ground after all against the tide of extinction?

Of course one must take some of these reports with a grain of salt. There have been Thylacine sightings within 30km of my home in the Blue Mountains of NSW, and around the fringes of Melbourne suburbs. Could these sightings be genuine, or are they merely just the product of wishful thinking? Perhaps they are the echoes of a recent past...marsupial memories prowling the wilderness of our collective guilt-ridden subconscious over an arguably preventable extinction event.

To this day there is passionate debate about the Thylacine's continued existence in the Australian wilderness: whether the Thylacine is extinct, already gone after the loss of a sustainable breeding population; or extant and still with us in small numbers, clinging to survival.

To further this discussion, Australia's resident experts and enthusiasts have come together in this anthology to put forward their assessments. This book shares optimistic, pessimistic and pragmatic assessments of the status of the Thylacine's existence and possible resurrection. Academics, amateurs and scientists all share this platform, putting forward articulate and reasoned arguments.

You will notice some crossover between the contributions as several authors explore the same famous cases, and ponder the implications for either the Thylacine's ongoing survival or indisputable extinction.

One such case is the unconfirmed 1982 sighting of a Thylacine near the Arthur River in the State's north-west by ranger Hans Naarding, investigated by then-Parks and Wildlife Officer, and contributor to this volume, Nick Mooney. Nick's observations about that sighting are shared in Chapter 3.

Another concerns the 1985 photographs taken by Kevin Cameron of an alleged Thylacine, which were vigorously defended by West Australian zoologist Athol Douglas and featured in *New Scientist* magazine. The case is explored in detail (sans photographs) in Chapter 4 by Tony Healy and Paul Cropper.

I would like to thank all of the authors featured in this anthology who have enthusiastically embraced the idea, and given their time to contribute to this project, and to the families of Ned Terry and Peter Chapple who have graciously given us permission to reprint their contributions.

Special mention must go to Joy Williams, Tania Poole, Tony Healy and Paul Cropper for their continuing assistance and enthusiasm from the outset in the preparation of this volume, to Dr Karl Shuker for writing the foreword, David Mattichak for his guidance on formatting, and graphic designer Tim Hartridge for another exceptional book cover.

My partner and collaborator Michael Williams - who (like many of my friends) shares my own particular brand of madness when it comes to pursuing lines of enquiry concerning the improbable, impossible and downright implausible – has also been a great supporter of, and contributor to, this project.

I would also like to make special mention of my fellow expedition members hailing from the United Kingdom and Australia, a party that included Jonathan McGowan, Richard Freeman, Lisa Malam, Dr Chris Clark, Orrin Hare, and Dr Hannah Jenkins (as well as myself, Michael, Tony and Tania). The support of the UK Centre for Fortean Zoology's Jonathan Downes and his team, and of Danish zoologist Lars Thomas, has proven invaluable.

Is the Tasmanian Tiger extinct or extant? Let us know what you decide. Visit **www.australian-tasmanian-tiger.com** and share your views and stories.

Rebecca Lang, September 2014

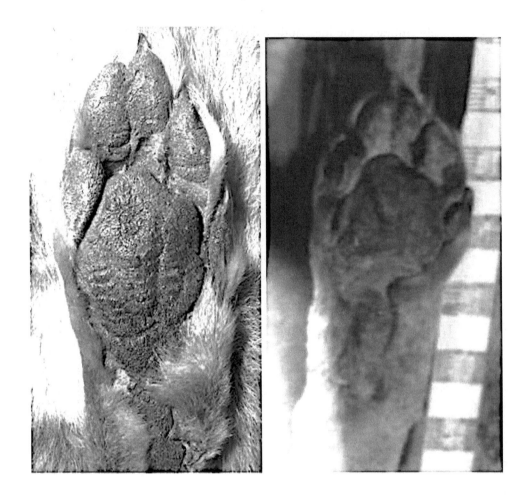

On the left is a photo of a preserved Thylacine foot from Oxford University in the United Kingdom. On the right is a photo of a foot of a Thylacine that was allegedly shot near Adamsfield, in the remote South-West of Tasmania in the 1990s. *Courtesy of Col Bailey.*

CHAPTER 1

The Case for an Extant Thylacine Population in Tasmania

by Col Bailey

My personal experience dealing with Thylacine research spans four decades and covers both theoretical study as well as intensive field investigation. My hypothesis therefore is based primarily on what I have witnessed, and through my own observations I am resolute in my belief that the Thylacine is most definitely not extinct. I don't think or hope or suppose this animal has survived to the present day, I know, categorically, because I have seen it in the flesh, and there is certainly no way that I could have been mistaken in my identification of that animal. No amount of contradiction will change my mind on this fact; I am absolutely one hundred per cent positive that at least one Thylacine was living in the South West National Park in the early autumn of 1995. I also have little doubt that there were more of the same in that isolated region of untamed wilderness judging by what I heard earlier that same morning. The fact that I have recognised that same strident vocalisation from several other areas of southern and western Tasmania over the past 12 years tells me there is every likelihood that at least two colonies of Thylacine exist to the present day and it is possible there are more.

I am confident there will be those, especially of the scientific and academic persuasion, who find my claims absurd and completely unbelievable. Such people are no doubt possessed of a rigid, inflexible attitude on this subject that renders them acutely narrow minded. Most though will, I believe, be rational to a point in concurring that, regardless of not being completely convinced, there nevertheless exists a remote possibility that such a likelihood is not entirely beyond the realms of possibility.

Perhaps the quintessential sighting report is the Naarding account of 1982, when NPWS field officer, Hans Naarding claimed to have witnessed a Thylacine at Togari in the far north-west of Tasmania. This sighting gained much prominence upon its release to the media several years later and today appears to have set the standard in post 1936 Thylacine detection. In addition, there have also been a handful of exceptional Thylacine sightings over recent years that stand up well to rigid examination. However, it appears that short of hard evidence, nothing will conciliate the scientific community, save a freshly dead or live specimen. Photographs, as convincing as they may appear can be spuriously manipulated and are in my opinion far from acid proof, for there will always be an element of doubt connected to such technology. Print casts likewise can be manufactured to deceive and confuse, not disputing the fact that when actually discovered in the field can be a most obvious sign of a Thylacine presence in the area. Likewise, sound and scent observations are powerful clues in themselves, but unless recorded or bottled, cannot be accepted as conclusive enough to absolutely confirm a sighting. Important too, is the fact that neither of these methods has been officially documented to prove one way or the other their absolute authenticity.

The typical somewhat intractable Tasmanian tiger hunter is almost a thing of the past as modern technology and the electronic age have steadily encroached on what were once time worn techniques.

The old established traditions have now given way to the high-tech gadgetry of today's world and with it has evolved a new breed of well versed and educated Thylacine seeker relying heavily on up-market devices to bring home the bacon. But will they succeed?

I wish to clearly emphasise from the outset that this particular activity is most definitely not something that can be accomplished or sufficiently understood in the short term, for we are dealing with an astonishingly proficient marsupial carnivore, a significant factor that cannot be too strongly emphasised. Far too many inadvertently believe there is little more to searching for this animal than to set up a few remotes along an animal trail and sit back and let their quarry do the rest.

They pay scant attention to detail, entering the bush reeking of various types of potentially environmentally unfriendly odours; perfumes and numerous other tangs of various obnoxious persuasions including, cigarettes, after shaves and deodorants, etc, etc, and making copious amounts of noise into the bargain. They pay far too little thought to these extremely important factors, much less to common sense in somehow believing they are dealing with some imbecilic, moronic, half blind, partially deaf, bumbling fool of a thing that has trouble getting out of its own way! Nothing could be further from reality.

The secret is to smell like the bush itself; to blend in with nature and present as unobtrusive a presence as is possible in order to best disguise and camouflage our entry. One also needs to be extremely patient, for patience is clearly a fundamental virtue in this craft. Any hope of detecting a Thylacine in a particular region requires a thorough recognisance of the area beforehand to familiarise oneself with the lay of the land. Clues by the way of actual sighting reports and prints are normally the main options in the evaluation of a given area, but it must always be remembered that this animal is an itinerant wanderer, never spending more than a few days in the one place as it transverses its vast hunting range.

For many years my study of the Tasmanian tiger was somewhat perplexed, being based more on hopeful anticipation than substantial knowledge and observation, the sole nucleus being the chance sighting of an unusual animal along the shores of the Coorong lagoon in South Eastern South Australia over twenty years before. To this day I am unsure that the animal I observed for some minutes in the early morning of a summer's day in 1967 was actually a Tasmanian tiger. However, local research revealed many other similar sightings of the same type of animal that was being roundly identified as a Thylacine. If nothing else, what I detected that day aroused my curiosity sufficiently to embark on what has since become a most significant journey of research and discovery.

Following this I proceeded to seek out written material dealing with most every aspect of the Thylacine, but back in the 1960s there was unfortunately little to be found. I profited somewhat from my late father's trapping experience and bush tuition and of his fleeting interest in the animal dating back to the 1930s, as well as his possession of a most informative magazine article dealing with Victorian zoologist, David Fleay's 1946 Thylacine search in Western Tasmania.

Subsequent enquiries eventually led to the heart of the matter in interviewing the men who actually hunted the Thylacine when it was with us in good numbers; the Tasmanian snarers and trappers, the bushmen and the farmers who had sought out the Thylacine for either monetary gain or pure revenge. Several of these men were true experts, having an acute knowledge of the behaviour, habits and general ecology of the animal and as a result were a literal storehouse of information. They had actively studied the Thylacine in the field, something that is unfortunately missing in latter-day knowledge, and it was from these men that I was able to glean a great deal of invaluable and comprehensible data. For some the Tasmanian tiger was little more than a 'cash cow', seen as a practical means of supplementing their often-meager income in putting food on the table. Taken alive the Thylacine was considered a rare prize, commanding significant monetary reward as they became rarer, while those found dead in the snare still attracted a worthwhile return. For others it was considered a pest, a dispensable menace to be eliminated on sight and by whatever means possible.

An interview I conducted with notable Thylacine hunter, Elias Churchill in 1969 proved a watershed, an equilibrium of sorts in acquiring prime information from an experienced and accurate source. Although many of the old trappers were still alive in Tasmania at the time, actually locating those with categorical hands-on experience in Thylacine hunting was easier said than done. Churchill was most charitable in freely sharing his information and I gained a great deal from this aging fount of knowledge.

Another of the old trappers to be of significant assistance was 80-year-old Reg Trigg. I came across this elderly Tasmanian bushman quite by accident in the summer of 1980, and in doing so was able to tap into a vast reservoir of previously untold information relating to the Thylacine.

Renowned bushman and West Coast mineral prospector, Deny King was another who shared with me intriguing and valuable information on the animal, and most importantly, divulged crucial knowledge of an area that was to later play an integral part in my discovery of the Tasmanian tiger.

On moving permanently with my family to Tasmania in 1990, my research stepped up a peg, and living as we did at Tyenna, once considered the heartland of the Tasmanian tiger, I was favoured by having a huge tract of prime wilderness country virtually on my doorstep. Despite my enthusiasm and eagerness to locate the Thylacine, by the summer of 1993 frustration was already rearing its obtrusive head. I had to then achieved little and was seriously considering shelving the idea of field searches and concentrating more on the historical side of the debate in writing up the many anecdotal stories I had acquired along the way, as well as interviewing people who believed they had lately seen a Thylacine in the Tasmanian bush. Then, out of the blue came a completely unforeseen bonus that was to reshape my entire attitude and understanding of the animal. It was in effect, my coming of age.

By this time we had moved to Maydena, a former logging town four miles further along the road and situated at the very threshold of the vast South West National Park, a hugely diverse wilderness that was destined to become my classroom. In the summer of 1993, I received an anonymous phone call claiming that 'an old bloke was feeding tigers on his Weld Valley property'. The call was brief and to the point, and the only information I had to go on was that 'the old bloke' was living in a caravan alongside a creek somewhere out near Lonnavale. At first I brushed it off as something of a prank call but for some reason it kept gnawing at me, until at last I decided to check it out.

To cut a long story short, after much searching I eventually located the camp in question and from this most improbable source came the breakthrough I had long been searching for. This 79-year-old recluse held the key to an untold source of quite astonishing information that enabled me to locate a living, breathing Thylacine two years later, deep in the wilderness of the Weld Valley.

This was not a chance sighting, as is almost always the case in these circumstances, but a calculated and deliberate act on my part, following instructions from this elderly man who claimed to have previously witnessed Thylacines in this isolated and wild area of the southwest. And it was most certainly not pure luck, although I have to admit that luck did play a significant part in it by way of my chance meeting with this aged gentleman in the first place.

I was there on a specific mission - to locate the Thylacine - and that's exactly what I succeeded in doing. Entering the area was not easy in itself, far from it. In accessing this rugged and inhospitable region, it took me several days to battle my way through some mighty tough country. I took a significant risk in going it alone, but that's the way I have always worked on matters as important as this. Covert investigation is crucial in the evaluation of information such as I had received, and the fewer in the know the better. I was careful to observe all the acquired Thylacine seeking protocol with this one, and even then, I was almost caught out by the unexpected and sudden emergence of the animal.

I do not and have never used remote cameras, not that I find anything wrong with them, but I am of the old school in having been shown the ropes by men who knew absolutely nothing of such things. My logic is, if they got worthwhile results by using the same tried and proven methods, why shouldn't I? As I see it, the main disadvantage with all of this high-tech imagery is not the cameras themselves, but rather the foreign scent they and their bearers carry into the bush. In the majority of cases, the carrier cares nothing for personal observance and only adds to the problem in transporting highly detectable odours into the immediate area. Because the Thylacine has one of the best noses in the business it will detect any unusual smell a country mile away.

Stealth is another all-important virtue that appears to have been sadly forgotten in today's world of almost effortless achievement. Where once an area was quietly entered on foot from a distance, today it is possible to drive a 4WD vehicle almost to the scene, and many do! What they hope to achieve in doing this truly baffles me, for any self-respecting Thylacine would have high-tailed it the moment they detected a vehicle trespassing on their patch.

Perhaps we are at a distinct disadvantage today in not being permitted to trap and snare, for indeed, was this not once the main line of attack in catching a Thylacine? While I personally do not hold with this now illegal practice, it was after all, the primary means of securing Thylacines alive for zoos and collections. It is therefore significant to point out that the world's last known captive Thylacine carried the noticeable scar of this method of capture on one of its hind legs until the day it died. The only other technique used in taking a Thylacine alive was the pit-fall trap. If trapping, snaring and the use of pit-fall traps are today illegal, how then are we going to capture this highly emotive animal alive? This is a situation that the late Eric Guiler and I discussed at length and an unambiguous answer was hard to find.

But at the end of the day, it is not something I would wish to be confronted with, because my sole objective is to submit conclusive proof of a Thylacine presence to the appropriate authority and let them then take over.

My foremost concern then will be that they are suitably qualified and able to handle the ensuing situation competently. And after having done all the hard work, I would therefore be absolutely adamant that I be part of any consequential action.

After my Weld Valley sighting, (which by the way was kept a closely guarded secret for 17 years) I then concentrated on evaluating a technique in plotting Thylacine activity over its territorial range that I identified as the 'corridor theory'. In discovering regular Thylacine movement along animal trails within a reasonably defined path of its territory, this presented me with a means of actually catching up with the animal. The tantalising question was, at approximately what intervals did the animal traverse its range? The real essence of such a contract is to 'be in the right place at the right time'.

I was later to put this theory to practice in a section of old growth forest between the Sawback and Ragged Ranges south-east of Adamsfield. Strongly suspecting a Thylacine corridor existed in this area, over a period of six weeks I regularly patrolled the region in the hope of locating the animal in its day-hide, wherever that may have been. Over that six-week duration, I became increasingly conversant with the forest and was successful in locating several potential hides.

One of these in particular revealed signs of recent use by a large animal. Into the fifth week I entered the range early one morning to be confronted with what I can only describe as an odour the likes of which I had never smelt before. It had a most pungent and noticeable tang, totally diverse from the usual forest smells, and particularly distinctive. If I had to compare it with another, I would choose the characteristic odour that comes from the red fox, only this was something different again; eccentric, bland and sharp, quite unique, but not in any way offensive to the nose. That odour lingered for well in excess of 30 seconds before slowly drifting away, emphasising the fact that the perpetrator had been there and quickly departed as I entered the scene. A thorough search of the near vicinity consisting of rock overhangs, and reasonably thick ferny undergrowth revealed nothing out of the ordinary, I am positive the animal responsible for that odour was a Thylacine, this based on in-depth information gained from certain of the old trappers who went to great pains to explain such a smell. I strongly believed that this particular area was a corridor and somehow connected with my 1995 Weld Valley sighting in being only some twenty miles across country.

There are basically three types of Thylacine observance; visual, sound and smell, and anyone sufficiently conversant with the Thylacine can readily detect the animal from any one of these. I have now experienced all three, having had actual sound observance on at least four separate occasions in varying localities, and each in an isolated wilderness area. Perhaps the most significant of these was in the Weld Valley shortly before I came face to face with a Thylacine. It came in the early morning hours as an awakening call, although I never fully realised it as at the time I was camped alongside a river and these distinct calls came from button grass plains further up river. If only I'd been aware to the fact that I was actually camped within a Thylacine corridor I would most certainly have been better prepared for what unexpectedly took place later that morning. A full account of this is written up in my second book Shadow of the Thylacine.

Therefore, on the strength of what I have witnessed since 1995, I am in absolutely no doubt whatsoever that the Thylacine has survived to the present day. Be that as it may, I am, as previously stated, well aware that my resolute opinion is diametrically opposed to the rigid scientific belief that the Thylacine is extinct. Nonetheless, it appears that as soon as I voice my opinion on this subject, I am duly challenged to supply proof to back up my allegation. My answer is clear-cut - I have no proof. All is have is my good word to back up my claim. But by the same token, science has no conclusive proof that the Thylacine is extinct! So I guess it's a line ball. It relies all too heavily on the 50 years and you're out accord. And that has been proven to be wrong on numerous occasions in the past as previously deemed extinct species were discovered inexplicably back from the brink.

Having spelt out my firm belief on the matter, the question then arises as to just how many Thylacine can we anticipate are out there in the wilderness? That I'm afraid is the million-dollar question!

I am completely convinced the Thylacine can inbreed without any significant consequences, for if this were not so it would have bred itself out many generations ago. Therefore, any and all Thylacines extant in Tasmania today must somehow be related. Whether this has had any major effect on the animal we shall never know until such time as it can be studied and evaluated at close quarters. It is believed to live in loosely defined colonies within a vast hunting range, but what we don't know is exactly how many animals consist of a colony. It is impossible to know how many colonies there are within the island boundaries, and perhaps the only real way to establish this is to evaluate the geographical direction of completely plausible known sightings.

I believe that the Thylacine has retreated to isolated wilderness areas from where its detection will be far less frequent than it would normally be in more traversed and settled areas. Therefore the western and southwestern sectors of the island provides far greater scope for such remote habitation, and from evidence I have gathered over the years I strongly believe this to be the case. I am not disputing the fact that there may be other customary areas, particularly in the north-west of the state, the Arthur-Pieman Conservation area for example, but some of these regions have unfortunately experienced far greater intrusion in recent years than may be comfortable for a resident Thylacine population.

And what of the future for the Thylacine? Cyclic global weather patterns have also to be taken into consideration as the earth once again moves towards a warmer period.

The last such phenomena occurred 8-10,000 thousand years ago when rising sea levels caused by melting ice reshaped low lying areas and reorganised animal populations worldwide. This will, as before cause the extinction of certain species as previous haunts become unlivable. It may well affect the Thylacine, but not as it did previously when the island of Tasmania was isolated from mainland Australia resulting in the eventual extinction of the animal on the larger land mass. As far as Tasmania is concerned, wildfires will be the major threat as weather patterns become increasingly disturbed and unpredictable, causing significantly more electrical storm activity and hence more lightning strikes. Such conditions can only have a detrimental effect on the Thylacine as its presence is progressively exposed and its territory decreases.

If at some time in the future it becomes possible to capture Thylacine of both sexes, then will be the time to instigate a semi-captive breeding program in a secure sanctuary situation, an offshore island being by far the most conducive. Whereas Maria Island was once set-aside for such a purpose, there is no valid reason that it could not be once again utilised for such a program. Strict confidentiality would need to be implemented in the first instance, but there is little doubting that eventually such a momentous agenda would eventually focus worldwide attention securely upon Tasmania.

~~~

Col Bailey is an amateur Thylacine researcher with no academic qualifications; his knowledge has been gained from extensive personal study gained in pursuit of the Thylacine, both in theory and in the field.

His research of the animal extends over 46 years, having commenced in January 1967. He has written two books on this subject; **Tiger Tales - Stories of the Tasmanian Tiger**, *published in 2001, a collection of anecdotal stories gathered from the old bushmen and trappers along the way, and* **Shadow of the Thylacine- One Man's epic Search for the Tasmanian Tiger**, *published in 2013, a biography of his search and eventual re-discovery of the Thylacine in 1995.*

An artist's rendition of the Tasmanian Tiger (*Thylacinus cynocephalus*) from Brehm's Animal Life. *Originally published by the Bibliographical Institute, 1883, pp 544-547.*

CHAPTER 2

Experiences From the Past

by Ned Terry

I am not a scientist or trained formally in any way, and the following notes that have been put together are the accumulation of knowledge that has come from more than 50 years of being involved with bush trips, hunting and closely observing birds and animals in the wild. The Thylacine has always been the ultimate challenge, and began in earnest when on a fishing trip up the Pine Valley in 1963, I found some footprints in some soft mud. Not having a pencil, I traced them out as best I could using the nose of a .22 rifle bullet, on a piece of paper out of my fishing bag. They were sent to Eric Guiler, who replied that they were too rough to form an opinion as to whether they may have been Thylacine or not! However, my query was recorded in his notes.

In the 1970s, after I teamed up with Alec le Fevre - who had seen five - and we made that documentary *The Search for the Tasmanian Tiger*, much interest was created, and over the next few years I was asked to help with the production of five films from various countries. These included two from the Natural History Research Unit in Bristol, England, and most recently one from Germany.

There were also several interviews and demonstrations of cameras etc, on local TV programs, such as the ABC's The 7.30 Report, and I only did those to try and give some credibility to the search.

All this publicity about the Thylacine - which I wasn't looking for - has brought in many genuine people with stories and sightings over the years, and despite a steady stream of ridicule (which is like water off a duck's back), has enabled me to tape many wonderful experiences of genuine people, who would not go to National Parks to tell their story. There are between 30-40 tapes and another list of people who, for various reasons, didn't get their story recorded.

It makes one wonder how many other people have seen this animal, but are reluctant to report for fear of being ridiculed, or don't want the exposure. There were only two people who didn't wish to have their story recorded when I asked them if they minded. Others were satisfied if only their initials were used in the recording. It should also be remembered that now there is no snaring and very little hunting, and in most places an abundance of herbivores. This means that tigers no longer have to travel across roads or venture into man's domain, where they may be seen when hunting for food.

The Thylacine has a number of peculiarities that I believe are associated strongly with this animal. These are my own thoughts that have been generated over the years from my discussions with dozens of people, and my own observations and experience. The aspects that were most common to all these reports could be analysed and listed as follows:

- The animal never (except in one report) gave the impression of being in a hurry. It always just loped, or trotted, across the road or moved off into the bush quietly;

- Various descriptions of colour were from fawn (Jersey cow colour) to greyish-brown, and always with darker stripes from the middle of the back to the butt of the tail. About 17 stripes (if counted), tapered from top to bottom;

- It had a pungent smell, mentioned about three times;

- Those in close contact with it said it gave them a funny feeling and made the hairs on the back of your neck stick out. Four told me that:

    o   It had short pricked little ears;
    o   When it stopped moving it would sit back on its hind legs like a kangaroo, with its tail straight out behind;
    o   When it did go to move, the first few movements (four or five perhaps) would be half hopping, until it got right up on all four legs.

Several told of this;

When hunting or chasing a wallaby on scent it would give a 'yip, yip' at regular intervals, perhaps up to two minutes apart. This was mentioned several times. However, if it was prowling around a camp, it would make a guttural growl, or more of a howling noise;

- It was mentioned (and I have seen), that the animal eats into a wallaby and also a sheep from the front end, cleaning out the liver, heart etc. It was also mentioned that a female tiger would chop through the rib cage of a sheep, particularly to get the kidneys and kidney fat for the cubs;

- Another habit described several times is that they will leave a wallaby or kangaroo skin spread out on the ground, after eating the meat. The same for a sheep - leaving the big bones. If a devil gets onto a sheep, wool is scattered about all over the place, but not so with a tiger;

- Many people have said how terrified dogs are of tigers. That is very common. Paddy Hartnett and Basil Steers give good descriptions of that. Dogs would come to heel and not hunt and get into the tent or hut, and cringe if a tiger would come around at night (see interview of Tom Barrett);

- A common comment was that the animal can't turn quickly, it has to turn its whole body to get around. Mick Branch, in his interview describes that well. However, Paddy Hartnett describes how he went to grab a tiger by the tail once (in his hut - see interview), and it turned around and took the end off his thumb - so he said be careful!;

  o Many people claim they have seen footprints. I always respect these reports, but unless the person is well informed, footprints can be easily mistaken for another animal;

  o The female, with cubs, never seems to be alarmed, always composed, when in a light, or in close contact with man. Several times mentioned.

  o The animal can have three moods -

  a) It is extremely cunning and quick to size up danger, particularly with smell;

  b) Over a period of time it can get used to human intrusion, e.g. people in a hut, hunters or shepherds after three to four weeks. It tends to 'sticky-beak' and gains confidence to come close;

  c) Just plain hunger, probably from old age, will overcome fear.

- Footprints to get confused with:
  o The most common would be that of a large dog;
  o The next one most like a tiger is the front foot of a large devil;
  o Another one many get confused with is the front foot of a badger. If the print is clear 1 and 3 should be easy to eliminate. One has to be lucky to find a print in damp soil which is just firm enough to leave a clear image. If the ground is too wet, the detail won't be clear. If it's too dry and hard there won't be enough imprint to show detail. If the soil is sandy, the edges of the print will fall in, making the print indistinct.

Examples of the cunning instinct in the animal

Alec le Fevre - date unknown:

> That's right, now that other thing indicating how cunning these things are, that fellow that got that little cub and he reared it, he caught it, and he reared it in the bush, right away back in the bush and it finally left him when it was three years old, you know? And when it was lying outside his hut, and he was inside, if anyone was going to come it'd bristle up and walk round the hut, he'd know it was time to put the billy on, and it would disappear altogether, and by the time the billy was boiling someone would walk out of the bush. They're just so cunning. But remember this, those days they was all gravel roads, now people rode horses or travelled in a bloody jinker (horse and cart), or walked with hobnail boots, and he'd hear that perhaps a mile away.

Bill Steers - 1930s:

> Paddy reckons they've got the best nose of any wild animal that was ever put in the bush. They can pick up scent. And another thing they were telling me, the old Dad was with him one day up there and he went to help the old fellow and he said the old bugger wouldn't stop to have any dinner or anything – he'd eat of a night and morning and that was it. All of a sudden he popped his head up and said 'what do you hear?'. He said, 'a tiger over there, didn't you hear him? 'Anyway, sure enough he said 'he is down the flat and we are sitting on the side of the hill'. And next thing we saw a wallaby heading down and out across the flat plain and he said you could tell by the way he was jumping he'd about had it. 'Anyway,' he said, 'we will see a tiger'. The tiger stopped yipping and he said, 'he's lost him.' 'No,' he said, 'he hasn't lost him. 'Well,' he said, 'he is not barking.' 'No,' he said, 'he won't go across that clearing,' he said, and old Dad said a quarter of an hour or 20 minutes after he must have went down around the bottom of the plain and back to where the wallaby went into the bush off the plain, that's where he started yipping and away he went again. He was that cunning he wouldn't show himself even in those days.

When there were a few more tigers about they seemed to have had patterns of moving around.

Whether it was looking for fresh hunting area or for some other reason - perhaps mating, I don't know, but will mention two or three that I know of and quote one from Les Skelly's experience near Table Mountain. They would move around on a seasonal basis.

- On the West Coast years ago they used to move away from the coast in late Autumn - could have been weather, or following the game.
- On the East Coast they used to kill sheep regularly on a certain property very close to a particular phase of the moon - the first full moon in April. In the 1870s and '80s the tigers were killing quite a lot of sheep at Cockle Bay near Dunalley, and it was regular practice to move the sheep off a certain run there just before the first full moon in April.

Les Skelly relates how they always came and killed on a sheep-bedding bank on or near 13th April every year.

Les Skelly (Excerpts from *Central Plateau Oral History Project 2/38*, circa. 1940):

LS: Yes. And that one I saw over in Jinks's there. There was a lot of shooters, but there was a big ti-tree run up, straight up through it, about a mile. Well, if you went down towards Allison's fence, like here, come up that, you'd always shoot when kangaroo was scarce, you'd shoot four or five kangaroo up at the top often, coming out ahead of the shooters. I went up there this morning to wait; put a gang in at the bottom of her. They went down to Allison's fence and opened out. And coming up - and they'd only just started and they was, I reckon, the best end of a mile, from where I was, and this tiger walked through, sneaked out straight away. And it come up past me.

DB: You're talking about tigers killing sheep at Serat?
LS: Yes, I could show you the place where they killed them. And it was always either or near the thirteenth of April every year. They'd kill these sheep where they're bedded, on the same four or five acres of ground, every year.
DB: So you reckon the tigers came back every year like that?
LS: He'd come round. It goes round in a circle, a tiger. Right clean around the bush. And they always come off the end of the Western Tier, over the mountain - Table Mountain – and across over the road, up the road here, Tiger Hill, and went across the river onto Allison's Tier again. And their food is - say there was two old ones and two young ones or so, and when they come on, about, round about the 13th of April - it might be one day or two days before, or one day or two days after the 13th. But that's an every-year job. They would kill four or five sheep. Well, every sheep, they'd get him by the neck – they'd take the blood out of him - every bit of blood out of him, out of his jugular. And if these couple of little ones that they have - might be two or three, perhaps – they've not got enough, another one goes in on that bare patch under a sheep's shoulder, and it'd tear the ribs out just

bite them through like that - open a gap there. They'd go in on that bare patch and take all the fat from round the heart of the sheep. He pulls it off and he gives it to the young ones to eat.

DB: So that's why you were saying that their droppings looked like fat?

LS: Always, mmmm. They only eat blood and fat.

DB: So, if you saw some droppings with bone and all that in them, you'd say that would be a ... ?

LS: That's a devil. You don't see bones in a tiger's, because he don't eat bones.

DB: Did you used to find the droppings around here?

LS: Oh, I have seen them, yes. You'd see them when they used to go through, when I was a young feller, like, up here at Serat.

DB: What colour were the droppings?

LS: Snow-white! Just like fat?

DB: And very hard?

LS: Very, very hard! You wouldn't know that it wasn't a stone, see. It was smooth - as smooth as that and as white as that. Yeah, but they don't eat bones.

DB: You saw a couple of tigers yourself? You're lucky to have seen one.

LS: Yeah. I've seen two in my time.

DB: Did they used to trap them a bit around here?

LS: No. They never caught many here. No, there was - they caught a few down on the Western Tier; down the road, going from Interlaken down. And - but a lot of these old blokes, they had a dog that'd kill them. Well, I've heard my father say well, he only had one brother like (there was only the two boys), and he was killed with a tree up at Dungrove, his brother. And they was up at Lagoon of Islands there, and he had a beautiful hunting dog. He used to go shooting every weekend, and kangarooing and that. And he was out there towards Mt Penny one day, and this dog that he had looked at the log he was standing on and knew there was something in it. And there was an old one, a female one and three young ones in it. So he - this dog - dived in and caught one of the young ones. He was a half-breed kangaroo dog and sheep dog. He was bred, like special, for hunting kangaroo and that. And out come the old one and a young one, and he shot that - one each barrel. And out come another one and away he went, this young one. And when they was all - the three was dead - he put the dog onto the track of the other one, and he chased him for about a mile and caught him. He killed the four of them, he got the four of them.

I have just listed a few of the traits attached to tigers that I have personally learnt and others that have emerged from talking to many who have had first-hand experience. The above are a few examples that illustrate how cunning the animals are, or can be.

My sole desire has been, and still is, to establish that the Thylacine is still living, and prove it to the world. Money has never been an issue – it's the challenge. So all the planning and hard physical work in the bush I have enjoyed immensely.

Meeting so many genuine people and working quietly by myself a lot of the time investigating reports, and keeping cameras operable, and spending nights in the bush has given me a wealth of experience and understanding with native animals, and at home on the farm with domestic animals. I claim to be just an amateur self-taught observant searcher, with the firm belief the animal is still there.

~~~

Ned Terry has perhaps hunted the Tasmanian Tiger further than anyone else, travelling to the Highlands of Papua New Guinea to follow up reports of Thylacine sightings. He has lived and worked in northern Tasmania most of his life, and has been an ardent collector of oral history. He is also the author of four books including **Tasmanian Tiger: Alive and Well;** *and* **The Great Trout of Lake Pedder.**

This piece originally appeared in the ebook **Magnificent Survivor: Continued Existence of the Tasmanian Tiger by Tigerman,** *and is reprinted here with the permission of Ned Terry's family.*

Provenance of material is usually a problem. The plaster cast on the left hand side, claimed to have been cast in 2010, is of a hind foot of a Thylacine of about 25kg. The identification was made by comparing known footprints of quadrupeds around the world, and the size estimated by comparing it to the prints of a Tasmanian devil known to be 11kg (right hand side cast). The problem is that it is not known if the print is authentic or a hoax. *Courtesy of Nick Mooney.*

CHAPTER 3

So Near and Yet So Far

by Nick Mooney

We can probably blame thirsty Dutchmen for our inexhaustible interest in the Thylacine. It was Dutch seafarer Abel Tasman's shore party, in search of water on the edge of Marion Bay in 1642 that "...saw the footings of wild beasts having claws like a tyger, and other beasts...". Ironic, then, that the prints of *Thylacinus cynocephalus* don't even remotely resemble the gargantuan pugs of *Panthera tigris*. Those prints reported hundreds of years ago were probably of a wombat – the only Tasmanian animal the feet of which might appear large and well enough armed to have a dangerous owner.

Perhaps those explorers really only saw what their subconscious expected them to find, exemplifying our need to have monsters, a phenomena elegantly evoked by the poet William Blake's 'fearful symmetry'. If you imagine you're too modern for this, read Jim Corbett's white-knuckled (and that's just the readers'!) understatements about hunting and being hunted by real tigers, or Chris Black's record of white pointer sharks in Tasmania and you'll find a more visceral self.

Whatever that Dutch crew were thinking, theirs was perhaps the first mistake that led us up the garden path concerning the Thylacine. Much worse was to come. Gloomy warnings that the species was headed for extinction were being made by the middle of the century, including one by the eminent scientist John Gould in 1863. By 1870 it was thought the threat to sheep was largely over, meaning the Thylacine was already greatly reduced, yet sheep farmers' wild claims of stock depredation led to intensified persecution. The Buckland and Spring Bay Tiger and Eagle Extermination Society of 1884 typified this hysteria but even this was soundly trumped by the mother of all mistakes thylacini; the government bounty of 1887, passed near midnight on 15 September mainly to shut up parliamentarian John Lyne, a well known exaggerator. What a sad debacle.

The consequent rapidity of decline and the suddenness with which Thylacines apparently disappeared surprised even those determined to exterminate them. By the end of the bounty in 1909 the species was already very rare and in 1928, on the back of a suggestion the species be protected, a police survey found it 'rare or absent everywhere'. However, sheep farmers still fiercely resisted protection which was only achieved on 10th July 1936 just a few months before the last known Thylacine died miserably in captivity; another appalling sequence of events. In 1937 the police were again sent to find if any persisted, the indomitable Trooper Fleming even proposing a sanctuary in the far north-west in what is now known as the Tarkine. But, nothing was done. Perhaps the anxieties of the Great Depression and the gathering clouds of the coming World War simply distracted people. Even when expeditions by the famous Australian naturalists Michael Sharland and David Fleay found what they were sure was evidence, people still just accepted that the species was gone, swallowed by the wilderness. Somewhat later, this laissez faire attitude frustrated the newly arrived biologist Eric Guiler to the point he identified the potential value of Maria Island as a safe haven. How ironic that Maria Island now fills that role for the Tasmanian Devil in the face (no pun intended) of Devil Facial Tumour Disease, a deadly transmissible cancer. Lets hope this is an ultimately unnecessary precaution.

Occasional theories arose that the Thylacine was simply a species ripe for extinction. Never mind it had done perfectly well for many thousands of years before being rudely interrupted by Europeans. Other theories have speculated that distemper, introduced via dogs, wiped out Thylacines; but such a taxonomic jump is well beyond anything so far recorded.

Some marsupials are prone to their own epidemics and there was comment about all the Tasmanian carnivorous marsupials getting lethal disease at one period in the 1800s, but there is no evidence and others challenge the claim. Even with modern technology disease can be missed and mistakes made. In 1989 the parasite *Trichinella* was found in a quoll near Cradle Mountain. So ridiculously confident in their passive monitoring were veterinary authorities that an 'outbreak' and emergency response were declared; never mind the specimen had been in the freezer for more than a year nor that nowhere else had been tested. Scores of local possums, quolls and devils were killed for testing but still no wider testing occurred because "it was not in the plan". Wildlife officers, however, persisted in that demand and the bug quickly proved to be everywhere. The emergency evaporated. Subsequent publications by veterinary pathologists and others never even mentioned the drastic error so little was learned and the confidence in human ability to somehow 'know what is going on' returned.

Certainly the current situation with devils dropping to about 20 per cent of their original numbers within 20 years (and still falling) because of an epidemic (Devil Facial Tumour Disease) restricted to them, highlights the risks to animals on islands.

There is a recent hypothesis that because of a weak jaw, Thylacines could only effectively hunt large animals cooperatively and that human hunting thinned the latter to the extent that successful hunting was not possible. The argument continues that, although Thylacines could default to small prey, this had possibly become too rare because of feral dogs and cats, the lack of food contributing to the Thylacines' extinction.

I can only buy this hypothesis as a very minor contributor to extinction. Firstly, the little hunting across western Tasmania was very localised, and Thylacines there should have been able to hunt normally. Secondly, early accounts of kills of large animals by a single Thylacine, let alone impressive acts of self-defence against hunting dogs, suggested they had far from weak jaws. In any case, a 30-kilogram predator, even if relatively weakly jawed, is still absolutely powerful (even a swine of a Jack Russell terrier can kill a sheep). Once we cherry-pick reports made when Thylacines were reasonably common and observable we enter dangerous territory.

Most animals predated on by cats weigh much less than 500g, probably right at the lower end of Thylacines' interest. Finally, although feral dogs were locally common back then, they were largely restricted to areas near people and could not have competed for food with Thylacines across the latter's range.

I cast my vote for a more ordinary hypothesis in which fewer eccentric contingencies have to line up. In my view, it is likely that there were originally fewer Thylacines here than most people might think, the vast majority were in areas Europeans rushed to occupy and occupation of that prime land was thorough, ruthless and relentless.

It is much more likely that feral dogs were significant as actual predators (compared with competitors) of Thylacines in much the same way that wolves, dingoes and dholes sometimes hunt down competitors and potential predators, a twist on the well-known dog-cat tension.

In addition, Thylacines may have had female philopatry, a system in which young males disperse to find non-related females while young females stay near home. Such a species is slow to colonise new or emptier areas because new females do not arrive in areas where local extinction has occurred. If mortality lifts or productivity falls to a certain threshold, the ability to top up neighbouring populations, let alone recolonise areas, is lost. The grim drum roll of extinction then begins.

Perhaps there was no margin at all for extra mortality by hunting, especially if coincident with a disease of otherwise moderate impact, and consequent fragmentation happened more easily than even I think.

But, clearly the question remains unanswered: are they here, and if not when did the last one go? To answer in reverse, two issues are particularly instructive – hunting and what it represents in terms of Thylacine population trends. At least we have hard data for the bounty system and captures following it - a rare commodity in this game. Bounty payments started modestly but numbers quickly rose from 1888, peaking in 1899-1901, perhaps in part due to a hunting surge as the bounty system consolidated. Numbers of payments stayed high for nearly 15 years then rapidly reduced with none in the last few years of the system. Perhaps then it was hardly worth the effort for the same old bounty. Subsequent numbers caught for high value export were also low until the last capture in 1933, the whole trend reflecting an apparent population collapse. Anyone experienced with wildlife harvesting would agree that Europeans' hunting of Thylacine is a classic of harvesting exceeding productivity, exactly what the bounty intended.

Unless animals are bizarrely restricted or super vulnerable (as in easy to find and no defences), the Thylacine being neither, hunting can only exterminate a proportion of the population. If hunting effort is reasonably consistent, then the numbers of Thylacine caught somewhat shadows or parallels the actual population in hunted areas plus a geographical margin outside those areas from which Thylacines were drawn into that 'sink'. The trajectory of this hunting shadow clearly overshoots 1933 (i.e. the last one was probably not caught then), but by how much?

The second issue to look at when considering an extinction date is the concept of Maximum Sustained Yield. Although its long-term application has been largely discredited via collapses fisheries managed via its principals according, the concept remains useful for discussions of the impact of hunting on Thylacines.

Some small carnivores - such as mink - breed prolifically and can cope with high levels of hunting - up to 33 per cent of populations per year in some situations. Medium sized carnivores such as cats, coyotes and foxes can still absorb high mortalities of about 25 per cent but large carnivores simply do not have this capacity. Anything much beyond 7 per cent per year has proved too much for the gray wolf or leopard, for example. Therefore, for what it is worth, I have provisionally assigned the Thylacine a maximum harvest rate of 10 per cent since it is, in trophic level, size, reproductive capacity and life span, a large carnivore, even if much smaller than some contemporary megafauna.

The collapse strongly suggests harvesting, once the bounty scheme hit its stride, was well over sustained yield because payments collapsed within 8 years. Let us indulge and assume this suggests harvesting was at 15 per cent per year (that is 1 in 7 Thylacines available to be hunted were killed per year). This puts the hunted population at the time the bounty peaked at the turn of the century, at about 1070 animals, falling to less than 100 by 1908; quite a fall if hunting was reasonably consistent. After the bounty fizzled out in 1909, in a panic that they might miss out, museum and zoo authorities started a frenzy of last minute collecting, which in turn reinvigorated hunting effort. Not that the switch from persecution to collecting made much difference to Thylacines.

If we accept that this reduced hunting still exceeded what Thylacines could produce, at the last capture (in 1933) there should have been at least 7 left in the hunted area, albeit a badly fragmented group. There still remained the 5-10 per cent of the original population in areas that were not hunted, a low proportion of the total because these areas were sub optimal habitat.

This crude calculation I make is based on an average adult population density of about 1 per 30km^2 - a calculation I make from long-accepted relationships between the size of a carnivore and the usual areas it needs. Thus, at the arrival of Europeans, mainland Tasmania's approximate 63,000km^2 may have had about 2100 adult Thylacines at a seasonal peak.

To me it is entirely possible that at the time the last Thylacine recorded caught or killed suffered this indignity in 1933, there were at still least one hundred Thylacines left.

So what might have happened then?

The Great Depression was a period where one of the few 'good earners' was trapping of wallabies for fur. Literally millions of snare-nights were carried out through the late 1930s, usually using the same techniques, often in the very same areas and sometimes even by the same people that had caught Thylacines. Yet, no Thylacines were confirmed caught.

This result invites the question - could 100 Thylacines be missed by this de-facto survey or had they already further decreased? I believe both hypotheses may have occurred in that they continued to decrease and those diminished numbers may have been missed.

Maybe the fact that most snaring took place where there had already been heavy, sustained hunting of Thylacines is the basic answer.

As to those last 100 Thylacines possibly remaining in 1933, my suggestion is that they were fragmented into small groups- some of which just fizzled out, like flags being brushed off a war game. The possible combination of female philopatry and accelerated land clearing, which created practical barriers to Thylacine dispersal, would be a real problem (we know even devils avoid crossing exposed areas). This is especially so given soldier settlement schemes and their twin bulldozer ball and chain clearing. This might leave us with 50 animals potentially in contact. Thylacines probably lived for nearly 10 years in the wild, and females might breed 4 or 5 times. This would give them chances to find mates even if occasional years were missed.

Once populations are so low inbreeding can easily occur and many factors, normally of little consequence to a large population, can overwhelm. But, inbreeding is not universally disastrous, even in the medium term. A range of animals - from domestics through cheetahs to elephant seals - survive considerable inbreeding. Inbreeding did not seem to have obviously affected the Thylacine in that their immune systems and fertility (two key issues inbreeding affects) seem to have been in normal condition. No particularly lethal disease was properly recorded and young animals were reported all through the capture history. Stocatic events (a.k.a. 'bad luck') can become serious at low numbers. What was occasional incidental predation (for example, on pups by devils) becomes critical because as numbers of Thylacines fell, devils became relatively abundant. We know that hyenas and big cats can be catastrophic for cheetahs under these circumstances, and even hyenas can put lions, once very rare, under pressure. The very widespread strychnine poisoning of rabbits, often in what had been excellent Thylacine habitat, may have been critical if there were just scattered adults. Strychnine is indiscriminate and scavenging Thylacines would certainly have died (as did many other scavengers); and yes, they would scavenge if they had to – how else would they survive in captivity, for example. Even a few extra deaths may have been too much. Like other marsupial carnivores in Australia, it's probable that Thylacines had a considerable physiological resistance to what we call 1080 poison but the change from strychnine to 1080 may have been too late anyway.

So, how could 50 or so animals be overlooked beyond this point in the 1930s, even to the present?

Many a search has been conducted, varying wildly in their instigators' motivation, method and claimed success. Most have been brief: typically, spot-checks of locations from where a sighting was reported. Others have been mysterious, such as a French expedition with its pet sheep as bait, deep in the southwest wilderness. Some have been illegal, let alone unethical, harking back to earlier ruthlessness – one example being the pitfall traps for which a searcher was successfully prosecuted. More humane were the disused giant cages, and a tea tree stand cleverly hollowed out to form a near-invisible trap I saw near Rossarden in the late 1980s.

Some searches have been very public, like that of Peter Wright in the highlands around Lake Adelaide logically using snow for searching for footprints, and the ones by James Malley, Jeremy Griffiths and THE Dr Bob Brown all those years ago. David Fleay's (the last person to be bitten by a Thylacine, and then on the bum) and Dr Eric Guiler's very different searches are the stuff of legend and that of Stephen Smith and Eric became a valuable scientific report. Intriguing has been the web book 'Tigerbook,' written as an ongoing search-report-cum-contingency plan by the anonymous Tigerman. Other searches were secret. In the early 1990s, well-known wildlife photographer Dave Watts and biologist Stewart Blackhall conducted searches at Wombat Glen and Lake Lea using movie cameras. At present I know of four ongoing searches, not counting those photographic surveys of devils and other animals, searches that might get lucky.

And, of course there have been hoaxes. I remember one ripper in the days of the Farmhouse Creek logging protests. A person came into my workplace with an amazing tale, complete with a detailed diary of an entire Thylacine family followed, this person alleged, to a den and photographed. But alas, on the way out, the truck lurched, the door flew open, and the camera dropped into a limestone pothole - never to be recovered. The whole innovative yarn was about trying to stop the logging. Whatever my sympathies, all I could offer was a standing ovation. I have often been asked about photos but none I have seen have been either clearly of Thylacine and clearly authentic.

I have been involved as a participant, and/or advisor in many searches, most notably one following the famous 1982 report of a sighting at close quarters south of Togari by the rightly respected wildlife officer Hans Naarding. I had to decide how I could maximise chances of detection. Automatic cameras were then clumsy, were unreliable and had high serviceability. Nobody knows what a Thylacine scat looks like so an option was searching the many hundreds of carnivore scats in the area to see if any contained Thylacine hairs swallowed during grooming. DNA testing of possible scats was then impractical, although we did unsuccessfully try to develop a bile salt test.

But the dense vegetation and plethora of old logging roads gave an advantage. It is well known that carnivores will often follow habitat edges, and this extends to the use of modest vehicular tracks, the trend being stronger with dense forest. Devils certainly demonstrate this – in dense forest their footprints invariably go along the track, not across it. I think tracks give efficiency of movement and may concentrate prey to a certain extent. Tracks and roads break the canopy, providing light for regrowth and grasses - basic food for herbivores. As the forest opens up this relationship between predator presence and tracks breaks down, probably because diffuse light scatters the food opportunities and movement is easier.

Upon frame-by-frame development of the movie of a captive Thylacine I could describe the unique walking gait. By my calculation, Thylacines walking would leave about 4.5 prints per metre. Using comparable dogs on beaches, I estimated that a running Thylacine would leave about 1.2 prints per metre. Assuming they covered a bit more distance than devils – say, 12km per day - and assuming half was walked and half run, they should leave $4.5 \times 6 \times 1000 + 1.2 \times 6 \times 1000 = 27000 + 7200 = 34,200$ footfalls per night: a huge potential resource. Well, that proved to be wishful thinking. The true resource is of course how many of these footfalls turn out to leave footprints that might be recognised and it quickly became clear that the chances of getting a clear Thylacine footprint were miniscule considering the hyper-activity of devils unless I could separate them.

So, I came up with systems of obstacles intended to filter devils. I used logs that devils would most likely go around, as they are poor jumpers, which the larger Thylacine would hopefully cross, in doing so getting recorded; another filter was two sand print traps within 10-20 metres of each other. The first one a devil encountered would get much attention – sniffing, snorting, defecation, urination and sometimes a euro-genital drag. That in turn would focus the next devil and the next. The result was that one of the pair of print traps would get trashed while the other was transited, leaving fewer, clearer prints. A further devil filter was a wallaby or wombat carcass (road-killed of course) off the track to try and tie up local devils at least for one night. Interestingly, while doing this I discovered that carcasses more than 20 metres off the track might be missed for days in cold, calm weather, so focused were devils on the tracks in that dense habitat.

I also had to decide on how big an area to search. Any Thylacine Hans saw might be anywhere in its home range. Following acccpted relationships of principles of predator size and area they need, and tapping into Eric Guiler's knowledge of Thylacine hunters' diaries, I estimated an adult Thylacine's home range to be about 8km in diameter (Hans reported seeing an adult male). To cover all possibilities of where in its home range 'Hans' animal' may have been, I therefore needed to search an area about 16km in diameter, about 200km^2.

Doing it again I would mix my search technologies using many digital cameras and DNA analysis of scats but I would retain sand pads and mud patches to cover the fallibilities of high -tech gear. I would also pick a place without many observers (meaning Thylacines may have been missed) but clearly suitable for resident Thylacines, partly judging that on the abundance of Wedge-tailed Eagles, a competitor needing similar habitats.

Despite a few heart-stopping moments with partial footprints I did not confirm Han's report but equally I did not disprove his report. My boldest conclusion was that there were probably no resident Thylacines there while I searched. I could have been wrong. And who knows what a Thylacine with a dearth of neighbours does?

Since that exciting time I have had decades of reflection on the circumstances under which Thylacines might have survived undetected, at least to irrefutable levels. They have to form a small enough population to have escaped such detection, but large enough to have medium-term viability. I don't think it reasonable to assign extraordinary cryptic powers such as they seemingly never had, nor amazing resistance to usual problems such as predation or inbreeding. Thylacines were caught or killed by many means. Nobody has harassed thylacines for many generations (of us and thylacines) so I also don't accept that there was enough selection for uber-cryptic behaviour. I think it more likely our powers of detection are simply less than we like to think. We only need to remember that Devil Facial Tumour Disease, a very graphic affliction in a large, common icon was over about 1/3 of Tasmania before it was detected. Also, I have travelled through Epping Forest perhaps 1000 times at all times of night yet have never seen a fallow deer there, although they are locally very common.

A common comment is that if Thylacines were extant, surely one would have been road-killed by now. Indeed, we know they fell into pitfalls, walked into traps, stood in crude snares and even entered buildings – exactly the sort of animal one might expect to get hit by a vehicle. That may be so, but the coincidence of animal and vehicle has to happen and happen in such a way that the collision kills the animal and the person must be inclined to report it in time to be confirmed.

It is widely agreed that any devil living within a home range diameter - say 4 kilometres - of a fast road is at some risk from that road. That buffer along roads actually adds up, amazingly, to nearly 33 per cent of devil distribution yet it is calculated only about 5 per cent of all devils are road-killed per year. That of course is because not every devil within 4 kilometres gets killed; applying 5 per cent of the total population to the 33 per cent exposed suggest it is more like 15 per cent of those animals exposed are killed.

If we are brave enough to make a logical extrapolation with, say, 50 Thylacines and assume they are as inclined to be hit, as are devils, then 5 per cent of 50 or 2.5 Thylacines might be killed every year. Although I know of 3 reports of Thylacine road-kills over many decades either this kill rate clearly does not happen and/or devils are more effective scavengers than even I think. We might keep in mind too that several reports involve people feeling so guilty they hid the carcass or at least delayed reporting so long it logically would have disappeared. Perhaps the risks to Thylacines are much lower than this speculation. If they indeed happened to live in remote areas, say dodging along the west coast with occasional use of hinterland, they may be at very little risk. Long ago I decided evidence had to be of a standard that would stand testing in court if I was to publicly support it and so far none has. I have been exposed to what one might describe as perfect sighting reports; even by a few by people I would trust with my life (even my beer!). Without doubt some people firmly believe they have seen Thylacines in recent decades but whether they did or not is the issue, sighting reports simply being unreliable as evidence. Options are it was a Thylacine, a misidentification, a hoax or an illusion and memory can be modified in many ways. Plenty of publications have featured maps of sighting reports. If we accept one sighting of a certain quality we must accept them all, and admit Thylacines are widespread not only over Tasmania - which clearly they are not – and even large parts of mainland Australia.

I also understand the anxieties of reporting, having myself reported a puma where it was not supposed to be in the USA and being asked was I sure it wasn't an otter.

Whenever possible I use reconstructions to get a measure of report quality, perhaps even getting a dog to do what the Thylacine was reported doing.

Peoples' judgments of time and distance, especially when excited, vary wildly from precise to woeful. I have found a common distance error of about + 170 per cent, meaning if someone says it was 100m away it was likely 170 metres. Now, at close distances this doesn't matter much, but it does over about 50 metres where detail recognition collapses. One report from the north-east was faithfully reported as 200 metres. That was a long distance with the naked eye in any case, but as it turned out the measured distance was just under 400 metres - an impossible distance for most people to see detail. Time estimates are even worse. From what I have been able to test, people usually overestimate by about 400 per cent. Most reported sighting times have been published as less than 10 seconds but in reality I suggest this is less than 3 seconds, perhaps helping explain why photos are never taken.

The Thylacine issue is a magnet for that attractive human trait - optimism. Most people half-seeing an animal flash across the road will think 'Hmm, I wonder what that was.' Others will think 'My God! That was a Thylacine' as much because what they saw was what they expected or hoped to see as what they did see. I've been in a car with such people when we had those different reactions to the same experience and remember a peculiar feeling of envy that someone could get that much more from a fleeting glimpse. That is not to say some people are not better or quicker observers than I; far from it. Working with my natural history hero, Nigel Brothers, I was constantly reminded of what I did not see first time, to be confirmed later by a second view.

Some people of course believe they have enough evidence and have even invented the concept of 'sub-proof' meaning near enough is good enough. But not so, and to be irrefutable evidence, has to be both testable and tested (beware the Ivory-billed Woodpecker!). Most of the material evidence I have seen has had abysmal provenance. A plaster cast lying in front of me as I write is a classic example (the same cast as in the accompanying photo). Loaned to me by a person who claims to have been given the piece by someone who they say cast it near such and such a place (in a large reserve). The reported caster confirms he did make the cast and claims it was from a series of footprints he found in 2010. All I can say is that it is a Thylacine footprint or a hoax. Whatever my feelings of his credibility (he is certainly an excellent naturalist and people I know well trust him) in reality all I have is his word and nobody can prove whether the cast was made as described or in someone's car boot, a museum, workshop or kitchen at a party. Far better to leave the print in situ until its context can be examined, or if that is not possible, take lots of photos with a scale then cast the print(s) with witnesses.

The other reality of course, is that such action is not always possible. Digital photography matched with email is a terrific tool, especially if sent unlabelled via intermediaries for expert assessment and I enjoy the challenge of nutting out such identifications. Years ago when a much publicised claimed photo was put to the test I was pleasantly surprised by the quality of forensics that could be applied to digital photos. Mind you, what to do with legally obtained evidence is a very personal decision and I respect it. The person loaning me the cast now has it back and I retreat to the attitude that my curiosity is of little consequence and perhaps the species is better off not being found.

Partially tested and unconfirmed bits of evidence are legion, and are far from restricted to Tasmania. The agonising thing, at least for me, is that the sum total of all this is a complete lack of resolution so I suspect we will be wrestling smoke for some time yet.

Are they still there?

This question is a major contributor to the shaping of Tasmania's social fabric - its parochialism and ingrained suspicion of authority; its enthusiasm for conspiracies when faced with uneasy facts or; and the instant polarisation and politicisation of any and every subject. In these circumstances many people, perhaps understandably, retreat to their own.

Every now and then I encounter an interesting example. I'll be filling my car at the service station. Another, usually a four-wheel drive, will pull up nearby. The occupant (always alone) fiddles with the pump and spots me. 'You're the fox bloke,' - the question becomes an accusation, referring to my advocacy for eradicating foxes in Tasmania. 'Sometimes,' I answer. 'Waste of bloody money that,' says he. 'There's no foxes.' We'll chat and 'agree to disagree'. When I hang up the hose, my companion will sometimes look at me gravely. I know what he's going to say. 'Tell you what,' he says and then comes the appropriate, dramatic pause, 'There's tigers out there.' 'That so?' 'Yep, my mate saw one up the scrub a few months ago,' and on we go. The original gruff approach is of course more a reflection of their lack of comfort at opening a conversation with some tosser from Hobart (i.e. me) but what intrigues me is that what their mate says they saw completely overwhelms the very considerable evidence of foxes.

How appropriate, that in its way, the Thylacine has screwed Tasmanians up.

Sadly, Tasmania is now not so big and there are few unvisited corners, but I have great faith in our ability to overlook things - even big things. If the Thylacine exists almost anyone might find it, or no one. But the most likely are those who are persistent and private, like the photographer Christo Baars, discoverer of devil disease (will we never escape thirsty Dutchmen?) or maybe one of the Thylacine searchers or even someone doing other wildlife surveys using cameras will get a hell of a fright when checking them. I had long hoped my friend the implacable Geoff King would be stunned one night at his amazing Devil Restaurant near Arthur River. But that wonderful man has now died and we are much poorer for it. I'm not sure I can find the enthusiasm to wish anyone else the same luck.

Certainly it seems necessary to most Tasmanians to know whether Thylacines are there or not but I cannot find it in me to fully cooperate with our western penchant for putting everything in a box. For me, that would be a forced decision, artificial and therefore somewhat diminished. Nor for me the fey, winking, wisdom that 'I don't believe in it but I know it's there.' I prefer a more open mind, the more boring 'it's probably not there but it just might be'.

The extent of the extinction process has occupied an enormous amount of thought; it still does, and probably will for decades. And, so it should because the Thylacines plight was common and not some bizarre phenomena as the hype might lead us to believe. It was a result of 'civilised' peoples' greed pure and simple, something still in motion all over the world. So, it is important humans are not too sure, that we find a bit of humility. What outrageous, anthropogenic hubris to think we could have caught the last Thylacine but it is chilling how many simply accept that is what happened. In any case, now that devils are in decline, wallabies super-abundant and, hopefully, land clearing slowing, any Thylacines might do okay and push up through the critical detection threshold and, for better or worse be 'rediscovered'. If they have survived 15 or more generations unconfirmed we should be ready to replace our enthusiasm for study and fame with profound respect. If they are gone then that is that. I for one am not particularly interested in a cloned freak show, more a celebration of how clever we are than anything to do with the Thylacine.

Had the 'tiger' been called by any of its Aboriginal names such as Corinna, I suspect it would have cut a much lower profile and perhaps not triggering the usual European predator hysteria, which sealed its doom. Perhaps they would still be just part of the Tasmanian landscape, something, given a bit of effort, we might all realistically expect to see. How wonderful that would be, to just once, give the finger to the terrible pandemic of extinction stalking our world.

At least some lessons appear to have finally been learned, exampled by the very substantial effort to save our irascible devils. But the improvements are not universal. Eagles are still sometimes shot and it was not so long ago, in 1999 and 2000, that permits were organised by a maverick public servant to a sheep farmer for killing an unlimited number of devils by poorly specified means, permission that essentially allowed the farmer to construct industrial scale, metal pitfall traps in which, until 2006, devils drowned, starved or fought to death. Thus, the barbarity that was visited upon Thylacines is just a scratch of the surface away. Vigilance must be eternal.

To cap the irony, not only did our wildly mis-named Tasmanian tiger become protected by law once it could no longer be found in the wild, it became immortal.

Acknowledgements

I would like to dedicate this essay to Bernie Mace and the late Dr Eric Guiler.

~~~

Nick Mooney is a wildlife biologist who has been investigating sightings of Tasmanian Tigers since the early 1980s on behalf of the Tasmanian Government. He investigated the famous 1982 Thylacine sighting in Tasmania's north-west by ranger Hans Naarding, and has been a frequent commentator on the Tasmanian Tiger in the media.

A photograph of a Tasmanian Tiger taken in Hobart Zoo, Tasmania, circa 1928.
Courtesy of Queen Victoria Museum.

CHAPTER 4

Mainland Thylacines

by Tony Healy and Paul Cropper

In the past 150 years or so, the vast, desolate, unforgiving Nullarbor Plain, so alien to Europeans, has been the death of many a traveller, many a stockman and untold thousands of sheep and cattle, most of whose bones have long since been ground to dust and scattered by the sun and wind.

One day in 1966, however, as two scientists were groping their way through an unexplored limestone cavern deep beneath the plain their torch light fell upon the remains of a creature which, though it had died long, long before white men even dreamed of Australia, was almost perfectly preserved: the 4,600 year old body of a Thylacine - a 'Tasmanian tiger'. Naturally mummified by the cave's cool dry atmosphere the carcass was so well preserved that its bones, teeth and skin were all intact: amazingly, even its stripes were perfectly discernable.

From that day onwards, the cave, on Mundrabilla Station near Eucla, WA, has been known as 'Thylacine Hole'. Its remarkable contents dramatised what the scientific community had long known from more fragmentary evidence: that in ancient times Thylacines were not confined to Tasmania but roamed all over the Australian mainland and also New Guinea.

Because the most recent mainland tiger remains are roughly 3,000 years old, and because no Thylacine has been shot or trapped on the mainland since the Europeans arrived, it is generally assumed the creatures disappeared from the mainland between, say, 1000 B.C. and 1788 A.D. Because dingoes were introduced to Australia - either by a late wave of Aborigines or by Malay fishermen - about 7,000 years ago, it is thought the mainland Thylacines died out after having their zoological niche gradually usurped by the more efficient newcomers. The dingoes, unlike the tigers, were capable of hunting in packs.

According to this theory, the Thylacines managed to survive in Tasmania only because that land mass was cut off from the mainland by rising sea levels about 12,000 years ago - just before the dingo spread to the southern part of the continent. Ancient cave paintings of Thylacines in Western Australia's Pilbara and in Arnhem Land provide clear evidence that mainland Aborigines were quite familiar with the animals. The mainland tiger, then, is officially as dead as the dodo. Like the parrot in the well-known Monty Python skit, it is 'deceased, defunct, gone to its heavenly reward, turned up its toes ... become stone-cold motherless dead. Carked it, mate!'

There is only one slight problem: like the Tasmanian Thylacines, the mainland tigers, though dead, refuse to lie down. For the last 40 years at least - and possibly for over a hundred - people have reported occasional encounters, on the sunny side of Bass Strait, with animals which seem to bear an uncanny resemblance to the Thylacine.

In all, we know of approximately 500 mainland tiger reports. Consider the following examples:

Near Inverell, NSW, 1937

In 1965, Jim Ramage of Mount Pritchard, NSW, told Bill James of Australian Outdoors magazine that he had seen three Thylacines - two dead, one alive - while working, at the age of 16, with his father and brother in the rugged, heavily-forested Staggy Creek area, about 30 miles south-west of Inverell, in the New England ranges.

> First sighting: Not far from where we were working there was a small creek in a gully. One day my brother told me: 'There is the body of a very funny animal down there. I don't know what it is!' The animal appeared to have been dead several weeks and we did not examine it too closely. At first sight it looked like a large dingo. The head was like a dog's only larger, and the fur a dusty brown colour. It appeared to be striped towards the back legs. The thing I particularly noticed was the unusual shape of the back legs. The foot appeared to be about four inches long. The animal also had a long thick tail.

The hindquarters reminded him of a kangaroo's: 'There was a similarity in both the back legs and the tail.' He thought the creature might have taken one of the many poison baits, which had recently been laid for foxes.'

> Second sighting: There were some other chaps camped in the area catching rabbits and about this time one of these men shot another animal like the one I had seen. He was going round the traps with a kerosene lantern when he saw the animal's eyes in the bush. It circled around and followed him back to camp, so the man got his rifle and shot it.

Ramage said the skin of the animal had been exhibited in two stores at Inverell and hundreds of people must have seen it: 'I saw the skin myself. It was hanging on a board. The stripes were very distinct, starting about three-quarters of the way towards what you might call the shoulders and fading out on the underpart.'

Third sighting: One afternoon, near sundown, he was walking back to camp along the edge of a bushy hillside. Over his shoulder was a sugar bag containing the weekly meat ration. Suddenly he saw a large striped animal: It stood there with its head towards me. He was quite a big bloke, about 5ft from nose to tail. He looked higher in front than at the back and the tail came down in a sweep, nearly to the ground -- (it) took off into the scrub ... it was more like pictures I have seen of hyenas than anything else.

Mr Ramage claimed that in 1964, when he first saw an illustration of a Thylacine, recognition was immediate: '... this was the animal I saw.'

Near Bourke, NSW, 1949

In 1968, after reading of the mummified Thylacine found under the Nullarbor Plain, S.J. Paramanov of Canberra wrote to the Western Australian Naturalist to describe an animal he encountered 19 years earlier:

During the C.S.I.R.O. Entomological Expedition, November 1949, I had the fortune of seeing the animal on the route from Bourke to Wanaaring, in an uninhabited area a few miles past Warrego River, where I was collecting on the right hand side of the road, only a few yards from the road. It was 11 am, and I observed the animal for 1-2 minutes from a distance of about 15-20 metres; it ran along the sand, which was covered with some very small bushes, the rest of the area being sandy. I saw the animal from a somewhat oblique angle, and the head was not clearly visible. Its size was that of a medium-sized dog, and the body proportions were also dog-like; it was uniformly grey-brown, with short hair; the strange tail, extremely wide at the base, seemed to be a continuation of the hindquarters; the hind leg was strongly marked with almost black horizontal stripes.

Generally, although dog-like, it was not a Canid, because of the structure of the hind part of the body. The most remarkable feature was the strange manner of running: although the animal was swinging regularly sideways, the hind part of the body made a kind of bobbing, up and down movement; the impression was as if the animal was drunk, as I had never seen anything like it. I hoped to find some specific characteristics from the footprints, but the sandy soil did not show them up; they were of the size of a medium-sized dog's imprint.

I made all the observations with great care, hoping to discuss the animal with my colleagues, but they unfortunately had been collecting on the opposite side of the road, and had not seen it. Later, back in Canberra, I came across an illustration of the Tasmanian Tiger, and immediately recognised it as the animal I had observed on my trip. The discovery of the carcass in the area of

Eucla, and my observation of the live specimen, convinces me that the animal still exists on the mainland of Australia.

Warrumbungle Mountains, NSW, 1971

One afternoon in January 1971 young Philomena Haylock got off her horse beside a big hollow log on the side of a scrubby hill just west of Mt Naman and was suddenly confronted with a 'very ugly striped animal'. It had big jaws and was only 12 feet away. She stood frozen to the spot until it turned and loped awkwardly away.

The next day Philomena and her aunt, Mrs Kath Haylock, were riding in open country just downhill from the site of the first incident when they came upon the same or a very similar animal.

They followed it up the hill and noted its striped brindle coat and small, round ears. Its stiff, lowset tail was thick at the base and thin at the end. The hind legs were very ugly and bent but the animal was healthy looking and covered the ground much faster than its clumsy, leisurely lope suggested.

Mrs Haylock, a skilled artist, later made a careful sketch of the animal.

There had been overnight rain and the animal left many very clear footprints. Mrs Haylock and a friend, Mrs Janet Finch, who passed this story on to us, took plaster casts, photographs, careful sketches and measurements of the tracks.

Curiously, all the prints from fore and hind feet showed only three toes and no claw impressions, totally unlike those of a Thylacine, or for that matter any other Australian animal.

Although they measured only 2 1/2 inches by 2 1/4 inches - no bigger than those of a blue heeler - the tracks were pressed very deeply into the ground compared with those of the family's dogs. Mrs Finch estimated that the animal must have weighed about 60 pounds.

Near Corin Dam, ACT, 1982

For seven years, from the mid-1970s, National Parks ranger Peter Simon patrolled the mountainous, heavily forested area around Corin Dam in Namadgi National Park, about 25km southwest of Canberra.

In 1984, 18 months after the event, he told us of seeing a striped animal as it moved across a clearing near Gibraltar Creek, about 7km east of the dam. Mr Simon had seen many illustrations of Tasmanian tigers and was adamant this creature, which he observed - at a range of 30 metres, in daylight, for several seconds - could have been nothing but a Thylacine.

After nightfall he returned to the spot and heard, coming from the bush, a very strange, harsh, panting. His dogs, which had been in at the death of over 300 wild pigs, absolutely refused to get out of the truck. Over the following 12 months two separate groups of tourists approached the ranger to report Tasmanian tiger sightings in virtually the same spot. Rex Gilroy has made reference to sightings at Tidbinbilla, just 5km to the north of Gibraltar Creek, and the Rare Fauna Research Society (the pre-cursor to the Australian Rare Fauna Research Association) has recorded one report from the same vicinity.

Near Pambula, NSW, 1984

In early August 1984, John Chevalier and his sister Sharon were camped with a small party of bushwalkers near Hart's Creek, about three kilometres south of Lake Pambula on the NSW south coast. At about 6.30 am they heard a 'low, coughing sound' just outside their tent:

> We opened the flyscreen and first of all noticed that half a loaf of bread from the night before had gone. We went outside and there we saw this large animal munching on something, probably our bread. It stood like a monument side on to us for about 30 seconds. It was as large as a Great Dane dog. Its head was like a wolf and its hindquarters were larger than its front quarters. It was a dark ginger colour and had vertical stripes across its back, which became lighter in colour towards its neck.

> There were three stripes under its chest and it had foot claws like a dog. We were flabbergasted. We thought, first of all, that some animal must have escaped from a zoo. Sharon screamed, I was a bit scared myself. We picked up a wooden stake just in case, but the animal bounded off into the bush. We followed it and caught another sight of it before it disappeared in an easterly direction into the scrub.

It is difficult to say with certainty when Europeans first started reporting tiger sightings on the mainland but in Australian Wildlife magazine, November 1947, a journalist called Morrison referred to 'persistent reports' in earlier years.

Although sightings have been reported from many parts of the country the great majority have come from the relatively well-watered, forested areas in the east and south-east of the continent within a couple of hundred kilometres of the sea. Within this zone there are several smaller and fairly well-defined areas which have produced so many reports of strange, striped animals over so many years that they have come to be talked of - among those of us crazy enough to seriously discuss such things - as 'hot-spots': prime 'Tiger' country.

Sometimes so many reports emanate from a particular locality that the press or public coin nicknames which give the animals a sort of regional identity. Probably the best way of showing the scale and on-going nature of the mainland tiger mystery would be to examine two or three of these hot-spots in some detail.

The Wonthaggi Monster - Southern Victoria, 1955-1993

(Seen mainly in the area bounded by Cape Patterson, Cape Liptrap and Wilson's Promontory to the south and to the north by Wonthaggi, Leongatha and Foster.)

At first blush, it seems totally outrageous to suggest that Thylacines (or unclassified animals closely resembling them) could be roaming wild in this coastal area only about 60 kilometres from Melbourne, Australia's second largest city. Although most of Wilson's Promontory is covered with bush (and is a declared national park) and although Cape Liptrap and other parts of the region are also quite well forested, a great part of the Wonthaggi Monster's supposed range is fairly open country. It is also, by the standards of rural Australia, rather densely settled.

Despite this, almost a hundred people - many of them pillars of the community - have, over the last four decades, reported close encounters with Thylacine-like animals in the area. The exact number of reports is impossible to pin down but the best-known authority on Australian folklore, Bill Wannan, said there were 70 sightings between Wonthaggi and Inverloch in the period 1951-72. A local journalist, Tom Gannon, told us he recorded 25 reports in a very limited area from two to four miles east of Wonthaggi between 1955 and '65 and the South Gippsland Sentinel Press, (Wonthaggi), of 11 March 1987 referred to over 80 sightings since 1955. When you consider that all of Tasmania has produced on average only seven Thylacine reports per decade since 1936, the scale of the Wonthaggi monster phenomenon becomes more apparent.

The Wonthaggi saga began in 1955 when stock began to be killed in alarmingly large numbers and in ways that seemed different from ordinary dog or fox predation.

'The appetites of half a dozen foxes wouldn't run to eating a sheep overnight,' said grazier Peter Atkinson, referring to an incident on his Outtrim Road property. 'Neither would their combined strength enable them to drag a sheep 200 yards.'

In December people began reporting glimpses of a large, unidentifiable animal and someone coined the name 'Wonthaggi monster' - a term the Victorian press pounced on. Newspaper coverage of the early sightings was generally slightly hysterical and very sloppy and some reporters seemed to allow themselves a great deal of journalistic licence. At first the press seemed intent on categorising the beast as a huge, striped, tree-climbing feline but gradually Thylacine-like descriptions such as the following began to predominate.

At 10.15am on December 6, 1955, Ern Featherstone, a car salesman, was demonstrating a vehicle to Mr and Mrs T. J. Schmedje only one mile out of

Wonthaggi when the 'monster' appeared. 'We had been talking about the animal when it popped out of the scrub in front of us,' said Mr Featherstone. 'It ran along the side of the road and disappeared into some scrub and when we stopped [there] it was looking at us.

'I've never seen anything like it. It was brown-striped, had a sleek coat and got along with a peculiar bound. It was about two feet six inches high, five feet long and had a tail as long as its body.'

Mr Schmedje said it reminded him of a hyena with a tail. 'It moved like a wallaby does when running on all fours. It had a fox-like head and a long nose.'

In January 1963, after ewes and calves had been killed and eaten on neighbouring properties, George Slater and Mr and Mrs J. Caldwell saw the 'monster'.

'It was about three feet six inches high and about four feet long,' said Mr Slater. 'It had a big, round head like a calf and big, broad, round ears. Its head was dark and it had fawn stripes around its ribs.'

For a little while in 1965 it looked as if the 'monster' saga had come to an end. On September 15 of that year, just one mile from Wonthaggi, Albert Sharp shot and wounded a rabbit, which rolled into a burrow. He was trying to reach the screaming animal 'when a strange feeling came over me and I looked around ... there, 25 yards away, was this amazing looking animal.

'I realised it was the monster. It did a back flip when the first 2 3/4 inch number three shot hit it. It also let out a cry I cannot describe. My second shot bowled it sideways. In my haste to reload, I dropped two cartridges. The monster disappeared into scrub.

'Its right front leg was dangling, and it staggered.'

In the days that followed the trigger-happy Mr Sharp received several blasts himself - from conservationists.

'As regards the animal and the individual who maimed it,' said R. Staub of the Fauna Protection Council, 'nature lovers differ as to which is the monster.'

In any case, it soon became apparent that if he really wanted to kill the creature Mr Sharp should have used silver bullets; sightings of the apparently quite healthy monster continued through the late 1960s.

By the 1970s most of the eyewitness descriptions seemed to agree fairly well with what we know of the Thylacine.

At 2.30pm on November 5, 1979 Mr and Mrs Charlie Thorpe of North Balwyn were driving in the Promontory's National Park when a strange creature emerged from the bush about a kilometre north of the aerodrome. It hesitated and then, without any apparent fear crossed the road in front of their car, according to Mr Thorpe:

> 'We ... were not moving fast ... probably about 40 km, and got a good look at the animal. It was taller than my Labrador but was lower in the hindquarters. It moved with a peculiar hopping gait. The tail was very thick at the base and longer than a dog's, tapering to a point. It appeared to be a dark to light grey in colour and had distinct darker bands around its hindquarters. The stripes did not appear to be black but were a darker grey than the rest of the body.'

When shown a picture of a Tasmanian tiger, Mrs Thorpe said it was definitely the same kind of animal.

In late 1979 the Wonthaggi beast appeared to extend its range a little to the northwest - bringing it to within 30km of Melbourne itself. Unlikely as this may sound, the witnesses were again quite adamant they had seen Thylacines. Two sightings allegedly occurred within three days in late December near the General Motors-Holden proving ground at Lang Lang and were three kilometres apart. Both happened around 5.40 am when the witnesses, Ian Garry, Ernie Hade and Slim Holland were driving to work and on both occasions the creature, moving with a loping gait, crossed the road 50 metres ahead of the car.

'We looked at each other with disbelief,' said Mr Garry. 'It had a long tail. Its back sloped away to its hindquarters. It was thick-set with stripes and it had a square head like a pig's snout.' Apart from the detail of the strangely shaped head, which seems jarringly out of whack, Mr Garry's description tallies well with what we know of the Thylacine. The creature evinced no great fear of motor vehicles: 'It just looked at the car without being disturbed and kept crossing at its own pace.'

When the men discussed their experiences later, a workmate, Les Doak, admitted he had seen the same thing 10 kilometres south at The Gurdies 18 months earlier. He had said nothing at the time for fear of ridicule. Journalist Tom Gannon, leading chronicler of the Wonthaggi beasts, commented that sporadic reports had been coming in from around The Gurdies and 20 km further south at Grantville since about 1968. Subsequently, in late 1980 or early '81 a Mrs Pateman, her husband and a Miss Davis told of seeing a similar animal in their car's headlight beams near Lang Lang.

Although the 1979 Lang Lang witnesses were sure they saw Tasmanian tigers, Ian Garry's insistence that the creature had 'a square head like a pit's snout' is, to put it mildly, a little disconcerting.

More definitely Thylacine-like was the animal seen by mail contractor Rose Bristow near Woolmai, only 10 km northwest of Wonthaggi in March 1987. In broad daylight

(11 a.m.) Mrs Bristow watched the animal for 2 1/2 minutes from a range of only 10 metres after it crossed Trew's Road ahead of her car. Although she stopped close by, the creature did not immediately move away:

> Its ears were erect and it was sniffing the air. After watching it for a while I got out of the car. It got scent of me and hurried back to the scrub - It was in excellent condition, and young. I did not notice whether it was a dog or a bitch.

Because the 'sandy, sable-coloured' animal was so unusual, she took great care to note its characteristics. It was too big for a fox and smaller than a kelpie, with a 'peculiar' head, dark stripes from shoulder to loin and a thick, heavy, unfurred tail. When Mrs Bristow, who has bred and shown dogs for 40 years, was shown a photograph of a Tasmanian tiger she did not hesitate: 'That's what it was.'

The only detail of Mrs Bristow's report that is not entirely suggestive of a Thylacine is this: although the animal had a dog-like appearance, its movements were 'feline'.

The witnesses involved in a more recent Wonthaggi monster report - in the Leongatha Star, 20 Nov 1990 - seem also to be clearly referring to Thylacines:

'Mr Sjoerd Reitsma told us that his wife and father-in-law had seen what they were sure was a Thylacine on Hillgroves Road, about 100 metres from the intersection with the Inverloch-Leongatha Road in broad daylight last Thursday. The two rushed back home and grabbed a copy of last week's Star, which featured a drawing of the Tasmanian Tigers, and Mrs Reitsma told her husband that it was definitely what the two had seen.

'My father-in-law knows animals and it definitely wasn't a fox, dog or regular animal, it was definitely a Thylacine', said Mr Reitsma. He said his wife and father-in-law had commented particularly on the unusual shape of the animal and the striped back.'

The Reitsma incident was just one of a series of seven sightings documented by Peter Chapple and the Rare Fauna Research Group in the two months to 16 January 1991.

Despite being shot by Albert Sharp and despite the passage of nearly forty years since it was first reported, the Wonthaggi monster appears to be alive and well in the mid-1990s.

Obviously, if the 'monster' is flesh and blood, there must be more than one creature; there must be a breeding colony of them in south Gippsland. As far as we know, however, there have been no definite reports of more than one creature seen at a time.

Crazy as the notion of Thylacines running loose in southern Victoria may seem, there is certain logic to it, in geographical terms at least. If the theory that the Australian tigers were wiped out by the southward movement of the dingoes is correct, then the Wonthaggi-Wilsons Promontory area - the most southerly tip of the continent - could well have been one of the last mainland refuges of the Thylacines.

Despite the large number of sightings that have come in over the last four decades, however, not a skerrick of tangible evidence has been produced to support the physical reality of the 'Wonthaggi monster'. None of the creatures has been shot dead or trapped. None of them has been photographed and, as far as we know, no casts have ever been made of their tracks.

The Ozenkadnook Tiger, circa 1885-1993

Somewhat more tangible evidence has come from another mainland tiger hot-spot: the border area of south-western Victoria and south-eastern South Australia, roughly bounded by Kingston, Bordertown, Horsham and Hamilton in the west, north and east and by Bass Strait to the south. This was, and is, the reputed haunt of the 'Tantanoola Tiger' and the 'Ozenkadnook Tiger'.

Although researchers now know Thylacine-like creatures have been reported on both sides of the border since at least 1960 - and probably for many years before that - it was not until 1962 that the phenomenon received widespread publicity.

In that year strange stories emanating from the immediate vicinity of Ozenkadnook, a hamlet in Victoria's Wimmera district, began to attract the interest of regional newspaper editors. The Ozenkadnook reports involved strange, striped dog-like animals and finally became so numerous that a Horsham newspaper, the Wimmera Mail Times, sent a reporter, Ken Hooper, to investigate. After interviewing several witnesses he rode into the bush with them and was shown large dog-like tracks that convinced him of the reality of the beasts.

Soon big city papers took notice and quickly christened the anomalous creature or creatures the 'Ozenkadnook Tiger'. The 'Tiger' had been sighted mainly in, or on the fringes of, a 3000-acre patch of dense bush and marshy swamp, which is part of a great scrub-belt running right through the Wimmera. Eyewitness testimony seemed to suggest the creatures were Thylacines even though some physical details and some sounds attributed to the animals did not seem quite right.

Typical of the early stories was that told by local farmer Cyril Tucker, who, armed with a .22 rifle, tracked one animal until he came within 20 yards of it. When it gave forth an "unearthly scream" he ventured no further. It was larger than a German shepherd and had, he said, a kangaroo-like face with a pig-like muzzle. It was grey with black stripes on the rump. The body was low-slung and the tail kangaroo-like: thick at the butt and tapering towards the end. It was larger than an ordinary farm dog and appeared rather high in the withers. The gait was a peculiar 'loping' movement - the hind legs appearing to move in unison.

Subsequently, Mr Tucker and his wife saw the same or a similar animal while driving to Edenhope. 'I will never forget the strange red glow of its eyes as it walked into the beam of the car lights,' he said.

While the Tasmanian tiger, judging from pre-1936 photographs, did not have what most people would call a pig-like muzzle, it must be admitted that that part of Mr Tucker's story matches the description of the Wonthaggi monster's head given by Ian Garry at Lang Lang in 1979. As far as we know, 'unearthly screams' were never attributed to Thylacines in Tasmania and the supposed 'strange red glow' of the eyes is at variance with the pale yellow reflection noted by Hans Naarding in Tasmania.

It soon became apparent to investigators that the Ozenkadnook Tiger (or the 'OK Tiger' as it was sometimes called for convenience) was not a solitary beast. Cyril Tucker's 16 year old son Stewart saw an animal similar to the one seen by his parents but somewhat smaller, and a yellow-grey colour beneath its stripes. Mrs V. Burns of Ozenkadnook also reported seeing a smaller animal. Wimmera Mail Times reporters established that throughout 1962 dozens of other people had seen creatures resembling those seen by the Tuckers.

On August 20, nine members of the Edenhope Hunt Club chased one of the animals through the scrub at Ozenkadnook and Stewart Tucker, who was along for the ride, experienced his second sighting. Miss Lee Lightburn, who also saw the animal clearly, agreed it was 'amazingly like the Tasmanian tiger'. A photograph was supposedly taken but at such long range that the moving animal could not be distinguished from the scrub.

Although the 'OK Tiger' reached the peak of its notoriety in 1962 it had, according to locals, been seen, on and off, for many years prior to that.

Howard Hinch, a former rabbit trapper and grazier, said he had caught glimpses of the animal as early as 1956, had often seen its huge dog-like tracks and heard its 'eerie cry'. He had lost full-grown sheep in the scrub and later found them torn to pieces. Trapped rabbits - and the traps themselves - had been dragged off.

Although they provided no documentation, the Wimmera Mail Times reporters stated more than once that reports of strange animals living in the dense forest of Patyah, near Ozenkadnook, had been made for 80 years or so. The phenomenon would therefore date from the mid 1880s.

The tracks examined by reporter Ken Hooper were said to be 'almost the size of a man's hand' but to judge from the photo, were about the size of a man's clenched fist: no larger than the track of any big dog. No mention was made of the number of toes and the photo is not clear enough to help in that regard. After the chase on August 20, members of the Edenhope Gun Club found where an animal appeared to have stopped sharply, making a deep impression resembling the elongated hind paw of a dog. They made a cast of the track, which measured 8 inches by 3, and, because they had by then researched the Tasmanian tiger and become aware that its 8 inch-long heel was sometimes visible in prints, were quite excited by the find. When the cast was sent to the National Museum in Melbourne, however, the official verdict was disappointing: the imprint was said to have been made by the leg of a large dog - either domestic or a dingo - in a prone position.

The wave of tiger sightings continued in the area through 1963 but no further tracks were photographed or cast. In 1964, however, a more dramatic piece of evidence appeared. It was a photograph of the 'Tiger' supposedly taken by a Melbourne woman, Rilla Martin while on holiday near Ozenkadnook.

Miss Martin allegedly saw the animal while driving along a track on the edge of thick scrub, 11 miles west of Goroke.

'I threw up the camera and snapped the picture,' she was quoted as saying. 'As the shutter clicked the animal bounded off into the scrub at a tremendous pace.'

Like the many 'not quite near enough, not quite clear enough,' photos from Loch Ness and from the stamping grounds of America's Bigfoot, the Rilla Martin photo is just clear enough to intrigue cryptozoologists and people already inclined to believe in the mainland tigers, but not good enough to convince sceptics or to reveal the shape of the animal's entire body.

There is no way of knowing for sure whether the picture is genuine but it appears to show a striped quadrupedal animal, partly obscured by shadows and foliage. Although, with broad bands covering its neck and shoulders as well as its hindquarters, it appears to be more heavily striped than the Tasmanian tiger, it could be a variety of Thylacine or something related to them.

The body, forequarters, hindquarters and tail, though partly obscured, conform generally to those of a Thylacine. The head is difficult to make out but, though seemingly more canine than feline in shape and though held high in the manner of a Tasmanian tiger, does not really look like that of a Thylacine.

Because her photo was given a hostile reception by the zoological establishment who simply could not identify the creature it showed - Miss Martin (now Mrs Knight and living in central Victoria) has since refused to comment on the matter. We will make further observations about the Martin photo in the conclusions section of this chapter.

After Miss Martin's experience the tiger sightings continued unabated in the Patyah-

Ozenkadnook area for another year. In early 1966, however, residents remarked that the animal's plaintive cry, which they believed was a mating call - and which had been heard in the district every July - had not been noticed that year, and that sighting reports had fallen away almost to zero. Mrs Cyril Tucker thought the creatures might have moved away because her husband and other farmers had recently cleared large areas of scrub.

Though it was absent for a while, at least, from the place that gave it its name, the OK Tiger or similar animals soon popped up elsewhere in the general area. Sightings were claimed at Goroke, Dimboola, Mt Arapiles and Casterton and in October 1967, at Brimpaen, near the western edge of the Grampians, two men pursued a striped creature for some distance in their truck.

The incident began at noon on October 2nd, when Bob and Wendy Rethus saw a strange animal eating a sheep carcass 200 yards from their farmhouse. At first they thought it was a dog but when they observed it through binoculars they saw it was something entirely unfamiliar.

As they watched, the animal chased away two wedge-tailed eagles, which were also interested in the sheep: 'He went for them and when they took off, the animal jumped in the air, trying to pull them down. Its hindquarters were almost three feet off the ground when it jumped.'

After lunch Mr Rethus and a shearer, Des Marra, took a utility and drove down to some low bushes where the creature was last seen:

'We hunted it out and chased it across open country. I was doing about 30 miles an hour but the animal kept about 15 to 20 yards in front of us. I had a clear view of it and Des watched it more closely while I drove. It was very dark brown and had distinct, almost black stripes running around its rib cage. Its fur was short and thick, similar to some dogs. The tail was long, stiff and smooth and curled back at the end. It had a big head with small ears. The head sat up almost vertical to its body as it ran, something like a horse, when it arches its neck.' After a chase of about 300 yards it disappeared into the scrub. Later, after consulting a book on Australian wildlife, Mr Rethus said the animal was similar in some points to the Tasmanian tiger.

South Australian Thylacines

In August 1967, after a group of children reported seeing a strange striped animal running along in front of their school bus between Naracoorte and Lucindale, the Wimmera Mail Times asked 'Has the Ozenkadnook Tiger migrated into South Australia?' and suggested, half seriously, that hunters and tourists tramping through the bush around Ozenkadnook in search of Thylacines had driven the creatures west.

South Australia, which is largely desert, is not a place you would normally associate with large, unknown animals. The south-east corner of the state, however, is different: well-watered by the roaring 40s blowing across the Great Australian Bight, it is a mixture of good farming country and forest, and is really a continuation, geographically and climatically, of southern Victoria. Its numerous areas of thick scrub and swamp might be just extensive enough to provide a safe retreat for a small population of large predators.

After the school bus incident, Mrs Dawn Anderson, the mother of one of the young witnesses, began to collect other reports from the area and was surprised to find how numerous they were.

'I think,' she said, '[the creatures] exist in numbers. I have had reports ... of two seen at once, and of animals with varying size and colouring, which would indicate different ages. These reports have come from highly respectable and responsible citizens.'

In addition to actual sightings, sounds – 'weird and sinister, like a woman screaming' - were heard and attributed to Thylacines. Tracks were found in the vicinity of some sightings and Mrs Anderson made a sketch of one, which appears to have the four toes and long heel suggestive of a Thylacine's rear foot.

As new reports came to hand, Mrs Anderson visited the locations involved and in the course of two and a half years experienced three sightings herself. In mid 1967 she and her son observed a Thylacine-like animal for 15 minutes as it moved along a ditch in a swamp; in February 1968, with 15 other people in three cars, she tried to corner one in a reed bed and in March she glimpsed one crossing a paddock.

In July of the same year she made plaster casts of tracks and collected hair at a spot on the Lucindale-Naracoorte road where a stock agent, Trevor Taylor, claimed a sighting. She claimed the casts showed that the creature's toes, like those of a Thylacine, were comparatively small compared with its large 'palm' pad. Since no mention was made of five toes, it seems there were four and that Mrs Anderson assumed the tracks were of the Thylacine's hind foot.

She sent the hair and casts to the South Australian Museum but instead of congratulations received a stinging rebuff: the Curator of Mammals dismissed the tracks as those of 'a medium-sized dog of a broad-footed breed, perhaps a beagle or small Labrador...' No further mention is made of the hair sample.

Although, as it was subsequently discovered, Thylacine-like creatures had been reported intermittently in southeast South Australia since at least 1960 and possibly for a decade before that, 1967 and early '68 produced a veritable flood of reports. Soon a local journalist, Samela Harris of the Naracoorte News, joined Mrs Anderson in her investigations and between them they collected statements from over 100 witnesses. Some reports were rather sketchy but some, such as that given by Parks Commission employee Jack Victory, were quite impressive.

Mr Victory experienced his sighting at a property fronting the Coorong, a long, thin finger of salt water behind Younghusband Peninsula:

'I was about 400 yards away, looking at birds through a telescope. I just didn't know what he was ... he was a large animal, a bit like a fox and a bit like a kangaroo. But he was neither. He started to run with a long, loping gait. He had a dog's head and a large tapering, rather stiff-looking tail. His torso was striped in grey. The rest of his body was brown.

'When we got to the spot where we had seen him, we found his paw marks in the clay. They were about the size of my fist and looked quite similar when I stuck my fist into the clay beside his imprint. We estimated his weight as about 120 to 150 pounds. The animal's appearance fits only that of the Thylacine.'

Millicent Tourist Officer John Pocock claimed a sighting in a private wildlife sanctuary near Grey, just outside of Rendlesham: 'It was a weird looking thing, with canine features in the upper part of the body and marsupial features, like a kangaroo, at the rear. It was striped like a tiger.'

Mr Pocock was rounding up emus in long, tussocky grass when he spotted the animal, which was sitting up, watching the proceedings with some interest. After getting over his initial shock he remembered a Commonwealth film unit was in the sanctuary at the time, filming wildlife - but by the time he located the cameraman the creature had gone.

Mr Pocock said his sighting was just one of many from the area - which is very rugged, with patches of dense scrub interspersed with water soaks and which is largely a declared wildlife sanctuary.

Naracoorte engine driver Don Gillette told of sighting Thylacines twice from his train near Lucindale and provided The News with a rather well executed sketch of what he saw. Interestingly, the creature it depicts appears very similar in shape and bearing to the animal in Rilla Martin's 1962 Ozenkadnook Tiger photo, although the stripe pattern is somewhat different.

Flashback - The Tantanoola Tiger, 1895

When the South Australian Thylacine reports began to receive wide publicity in 1967 local historians were quick to retell the legend of the 'Tantanoola Tiger', a creature which cut a bloody swathe through the sheep population of the south-east for two or three years up to 1895, when it was supposedly shot.

The Tantanoola saga, however, is a frustrating hodgepodge of fact and folklore, journalistic licence and outright fabrication.

The 'Tiger's' depredations appear to have begun about 1893 and at the height of its reign of terror it was held responsible for killing up to 50 sheep a night. Large tracks were found and it seems many settlers really thought a Bengal tiger was loose in the area. Women and children were kept inside as parties of armed men scoured the district.

Several people apparently sighted the creature, but names are not supplied and details are a bit sketchy. One man described it, rather melodramatically, as 'grinning, yellow and gleaming with satin stripes', and a youth riding home from a dance was said to have seen a great beast leap a high fence with a sheep gripped in its jaws.

A local schoolteacher supposedly reported that one night during a storm he heard noises in his kitchen. Jumping from his bed to investigate, he saw a huge animal leap through the open doorway. 'It was a tiger,' he declared.

The mystery was supposedly solved on August 21, 1895 when Tom (or 'Foss') Donovan dropped the tiger with his .44 Winchester at Mt Salt, 19 miles from Tantanoola. The dead animal, however, was no Bengal tiger - it was a dog - but rather an unusual looking one. It is often said that it was identified as an "Assyrian" or simply 'Syrian' wolf, but the expert who supposedly made this identification is never named. It is often said also that the wolf was believed to have swum ashore from the ship Helena that foundered about 20 miles from Tantanoola.

Whatever its true ancestry, the animal was stuffed and has been on display ever since in a glass case at the Tiger Hotel in Tantanoola. Whether it is a Syrian or any other kind of wolf we cannot say, but it is certainly not a remarkably large animal - only about the size of a German shepherd - and its coat is not in the least striped.

Apart from Foss Donovan's insistence that it was the mysterious predator and the apparent tapering-off of sheep deaths about the time it was killed there is little to suggest the dog in the glass case is in fact the dreaded 'Tiger'. In fact several witnesses vehemently denied that the creature shot by Donovan was in any way similar to the fearsome animal they saw in the wild.

That the animal is in any way exotic is, in fact, quite doubtful. In 1957 a 90-year-old pioneer, Alf Warman of Adelaide, happened to visit the Tiger Hotel and as soon as he laid eyes on the animal in the glass case he shouted: 'That's my dog!'

He claimed that when he was a young man his brother Ted gave him a puppy, which was the offspring of a European deerhound and a Bloodhound. The dog soon grew too large and expensive to feed, so Alf sent it to some acquaintances in the southeast that intended to use it, ironically enough, to help in the tracking and killing of wild dogs. The 'tiger' reports began soon afterwards. Mr Warman's story sounds good - but like everything else to do with the 'Tiger' it is not entirely satisfactory: to our eyes, the not particularly huge creature in the glass case looks nothing like a bloodhound and nothing like a deerhound.

So many years have gone by that it is impossible, in the case of the Tantanoola Tiger, to separate myth from reality. Perhaps a pack of wild dogs killed the sheep and moved on after the leader was killed; perhaps Thylacines were involved and for some reason kept a low profile between 1895 and 1961. The term 'tiger' may have been prompted by a fleeting glimpse of a Thylacine's striped back but may also have been used simply because it goes well with 'Tantanoola'. Had the 1890s outbreak occurred near, say, Lucindale, the phantom creature might well have been christened the 'Lucindale Leopard'.

One person who is familiar with the dog in the glass case and who also claims sightings of Thylacine-like animals in recent times has made a direct comparison between them. J.B. Pascoe, who glimpsed strange quadrupeds three times near Port MacDonnell between 1950 and 1960 stated, 'It was nothing like the notorious Tantanoola Tiger. It was quite a bit bigger, had a stiff tail and seemed to be weak in the back legs. It seemed to be more like the Tasmanian tiger.'

South Australian Thylacines 1970-93

Thylacine sightings continued to be reported in the southeast throughout the 1970s and two local residents; Kath Alcock and Mrs Dorothy Parker assisted Dawn Anderson in documenting them. The animals seen were usually thought to be full-grown or near full-grown but on the night of 1 November 1974 Barbara Adams of Frances and her children had a close encounter with some much younger animals.

The night was brilliantly moonlit and at 9.45 pm, as they drove past the Frances Gun Club, they saw two small animals ahead of them, playing on the edge of the dirt road. The pups were so preoccupied with their scuffling that they did not run away until the car approached to within just a few feet.

'We could have touched them,' Mrs Adams claimed. She and her four children agreed the animals were 'About 12 inches tall, sandy in colour with dark markings on the flank, too heavy in the hind-quarters to be foxes, heads like lion cubs with small ears; tails smooth and hanging in a downward curve or ellipse.' After checking a book on Australian marsupials they were satisfied the pups resembled Tasmanian tigers.

At 5pm on December 26 Peter Knight almost ran over a somewhat larger animal in almost the same spot. He said it was golden with dark stripes, round ears, and a bit smaller than a whippet. Four years earlier, after reports of strange animals in the same area, Mrs Parker had found, in soft sand, an 'absolutely perfect' track showing the five toes typical of Thylacine's front foot. Inexplicably, however, she failed to photograph or cast it.

In June 1975 a Thylacine was sighted near a flock of sheep at Comaum. Kath Alcock investigated and found that several sheep and lambs had been killed in the district at about the same time. They had been fed upon in a way reminiscent of the Thylacine: the blood had been sucked from their bodies.

Reports of Thylacine-like animals continued to come in from south-eastern South Australia right through the 1980s and eventually the phenomenon came to be taken seriously by some government officers such as Dr Tony Robinson of the National Parks and Wildlife Service, who accumulated quite a dossier of reports in the late 1980s.Sad to say, despite the often excellent eye-witness testimony dating back so many years and despite the efforts of all the investigators, both government and private, very little in the way of tangible evidence has ever been produced to support the existence of Thylacines in South Australia.

Cape Nelson, Victoria, 1971-74

Although few reports have come, in recent years, from the 'Tiger's' old hunting grounds in the immediate vicinity of Ozenkadnook, Thylacine sightings have continued to be reported on the Victorian side of the border throughout the 1970s, '80s and into the '90s. One particularly intense outbreak occurred at Cape Nelson, just south of Portland in the early 1970s, when farmers and road crews told of repeated close encounters with large, striped quadrupeds.

A description given by a piggery owner, Bob Herbertson - who claimed six separate sightings in early 1971 - was, though rather colourful, not entirely inconsistent with what we know of the Thylacine. It was, he said, 'strange, grey and furry', with stripes running around its rib cage and was 2 to 3 feet high. It had the muzzle of a dog, the rest of the head and forequarters of a cat, with powerful hindquarters and tail almost like those of a kangaroo. It covered the ground in tremendous bounds.

Andrew and Dora Murrell examined a similar animal through binoculars at their farm, three kilometres from the Cape Nelson lighthouse. It was half as big again as a fox, was tall, long and thin, with a tail almost as long as the body. It was dark brown with 'lines or bands' around the body.

The jaw 'was like that of a dog but it had ears like a fox. It was about a hundred metres from the house and we watched it for about five minutes before it ambled off back towards the lighthouse'.

At least one organised party, which included a Fisheries and Wildlife officer, attempted to search the area but were thwarted time and again by the thickness of the scrub and the roughness of the terrain.

Sightings became so numerous at one time that at least one road worker, Graham Mibus, began to take a camera to work with him. Predictably, perhaps, 'Murphy's Law' immediately came into operation: Mr Mibus, who had seen the creature at close range on two previous occasions, never so much as glimpsed it again.

Sightings of Thylacine-like creatures continue to be reported from the South Australia/Victoria border region up to the present day. Exciting as the eyewitness testimony is, and intriguing as 19th century stories about the Tantanoola Tiger certainly are, it has to be admitted that apart from several intriguing sketches by eyewitnesses and some footprint casts the only evidence which could be described as tangible is the 1964 Rilla Martin photo.

We believe the Martin photo could be genuine. Also on the positive side, we feel there are, in the South Australian and Victorian eyewitness testimony, certain distinct patterns, which indicate the mainland tiger phenomenon is more than a protracted series of hoaxes or hallucinations. These patterns, and the Martin photo, will be discussed in some detail at the end of this chapter.

WA Thylacines

Any readers who have had trouble accepting stories of Tasmanian tiger sightings in southern Victoria and south-east South Australia will find the location of the next mainland Thylacine 'hot spot' even harder to accept.

South-west Western Australia could hardly be further from Tasmania - Perth is almost as far from Hobart as Darwin is - and the suggestion that Thylacines could still exist there seems, at first blush, to be utterly absurd.

When the following four factors are taken into consideration, however, the possibility begins to seem a little less remote. Firstly, southeast Western Australia is - unlike most of the state - well watered and quite heavily forested. Secondly, 'Thylacine Hole' - the cave in which the 4,500 year old tiger carcass mentioned earlier was discovered - is in Western Australia, albeit in the south-eastern rather than the south-western corner of that huge state. Furthermore, Thylacine bones have been found at six other Western Australian locations. Thirdly, ancient Aboriginal pictographs of Thylacines have been found at three different sites in the state. Finally, in a paper which, surprisingly, received almost no attention from the popular press, Dr Michael Archer said that bones found alongside a Thylacine humerus (shoulder bone) in the Kimberleys in 1970 had been dated at less than 80 years old.

The West Australian Thylacine phenomenon came to the attention of the general public in a way quite similar to the emergence of the South Australian and Victorian tiger stories.

It seemed to begin about 1969, when reports of Tasmanian tiger sightings started to appear intermittently in regional newspapers. Next a handful of interested local people began collecting reports and footprint casts. They also did research which uncovered references to WA Thylacine sightings and slayings in earlier decades. The story began to feature in national newspapers and reached a climax when photographs of what may or may not have been Thylacines were taken and displayed. When Western Australian Thylacine sightings began to be reported fairly regularly in the early 1970s the location mentioned most frequently was the Nannup district, a forested area between Busselton and Manjimup, about 180 miles south of Perth. One of the first sightings occurred in 1966 when Tom Longbottom, a local farmer, saw one on his property:

'I had the lights all on when I heard something in the calf yard. When I went to look there it was. I stood and looked at it for 2-3 minutes before it ambled out of the yard. I was no more than 15-20 feet away from him. It was about the size of a roo dog with a big head, long body, heavy shoulders, long tail with brush on the last 12-14 inches or so. Some dark bands went around the body as well, eyes were not like dogs' eyes.

'I have been in the bush all my life and never seen anything like this before. It came back quite often for milk I left in a dish. I made a trap but never got him. 'The tracks were not dog tracks. We hear funny sounds at night like a choking or a soft barking, which I'd say was him. Our dog ... had a big fight in the roadway but he won't go out any more. I don't blame him.'

There were only one or two other sightings in the '60s but in a short period just preceding October 1970 several people reported seeing striped dog-like animals around Nannup, mainly in a large pine plantation six miles north of town.

Although some of the newspaper reports are frustratingly vague it seems most witnesses said the animals were '... dark, striped, with a long tail, fast-moving and about the size of a big dog' - and it seems some locals, quite early in the piece, suspected the creatures were related to the Thylacine.

Intrigued by the reports, forty people set out one Saturday morning in late October to hunt the 'Nannup Tiger'. The highlight - or perhaps low point - of the day came when the searchers fell victim to a practical joke: a sheep, shorn to the shoulders, painted with stripes and with long hair tied to its tail, had been put where it would be found.

'It looked like the real thing and caused quite a stir,' admitted David Blythe, the hunt's organiser. The day was not entirely wasted, however, as a sizeable lair was found and a plaster cast of what was considered to be an unusual four-toed track, similar to footprints found some months earlier, was made.

Although they never experienced a sighting themselves, Mr Blythe and his wife Pat remained convinced of the Thylacine's existence and continued to document all sightings in the area.

When the dust settled after the 'Nannup Tiger' safari, sighting reports of varying quality continued to be made. Some, such as that in which Bill Lavis and two other timber workers told of seeing a creature resembling '... a cross between a fox, a dog and a cat' were frustratingly sketchy. Others, such as that made by Freda and Joe Carmody in November 1972 were of considerable interest.

The Carmody incident occurred between Bridgetown and Nannup:

> ... the animal started to cross the road (it was 6 pm at the end of a very hot day and it had evidently been going down to a nearby pool to drink) and only noticed when our car was almost on it. Then it leapt around in the middle of the road with a most unusual bound more like a kangaroo than anything and loped off ... in no great hurry, with its head turned towards us, and finally disappeared into a growing crop.

It was a 'grand, upstanding creature'. They particularly noticed the broad head, neck and shoulders, all much heavier and stronger than any familiar animal and were scornful of the 'mangy fox' explanation often used by officialdom: 'Both my husband and I,' said Freda Carmody, 'are pretty keen on the bush and were both raised in the country, seeing enough dingoes and foxes to know what they look like.'

The couple were within 30 feet of the animal and said it looked exactly like photographs of Tasmanian Thylacines.

Their sighting so impressed the Carmodys that it literally changed their lives, inspiring them to set out on a quest through Western Australia, South Australia, Victoria, NSW and Tasmania for proof of the Thylacine's survival. Although tangible evidence eluded them, the energetic couple, in collaboration with Pat and David Blythe, collected a great deal of testimonial and archival material to add to the mainland tiger file.

Because their claims were modest and their approach low-key, the activities of the Blythes and the Carmodys attracted rather sympathetic but minimal press coverage. Then, in the early 1980s, the media discovered Sid Slee, of Hillside farm, Yoongarillup, who made for much more exciting reading.

Although Mr Slee's claims put those of previous tiger researchers in the shade and may appear preposterous to some, the West Australian newspapers gave him a fair hearing and we intend to do the same - because what he says about the colouration of the beasts, if true, is an important clue to the real identity of the mainland 'tigers'.

Mr Slee insists he has seen the animals 'many, many times' since about 1940 and that on two occasions has examined the carcass of dead Thylacines. He has discovered kangaroos with their heads chewed right off and has found the Thylacines' distinctive five-toed tracks on many occasions. All this has allegedly occurred within the confines of his own boundary fence.

In the mid 1970s, tiring of his neighbours' scepticism and ridicule, he hung a defiant sign on his front verandah:

'HILLSIDE - The Haunt of the Marsupial Wolf'

According to Mr Slee the Thylacines have lived at Hillside on and off for many years and take refuge in two large, virtually impenetrable thickets. Throughout the 1940s he glimpsed Thylacines near these thickets on many occasions and thought them responsible for the mauling of seven young heifers and many kangaroos found dead on the property during the war years.

His best sighting of a live animal did not occur until 1972 when, as he was doing his morning rounds, a large Thylacine appeared right in front of him. It was tall, thin but muscular, light yellow with a chocolate stripe down the spine and six or seven stripes on the hindquarters; the tail was dark and apparently hairless. From nose to tail it measured about seven feet. The animal was so close that when it turned to run it kicked gravel over his shoes.

As it ran, the farmer noted several interesting features: it moved both back legs in unison like a rabbit or kangaroo, and, when it glanced back at him over its right shoulder, '... its tail moved to the left to keep perfect balance.'

Although Mr Slee's encounters with live animals are interesting enough the most remarkable elements of his story relate to his supposed discovery of dead Thylacines.

The first such incident occurred one day in 1940 when he set out to search an area where a shooter claimed to have wounded a fox. To his amazement, he found, not a fox, but the body of a creature '... longer and thinner than a fox with light yellow biscuit-coloured hair one inch long covering its body and a stiff, almost hairless tail which was darker in colour'. Although it was not striped he knew it was not merely a feral dog because it had the form of a '... part dog, part cat and part kangaroo'.

The most interesting part of this report is the absence of stripes on the animal. This would indicate, fairly clearly, that the mainland Thylacines are not the descendants of Tasmanian tigers brought over from the island state and released prior to 1936 - as was suggested by Mrs Anderson in South Australia - but an entirely separate species.

The second dead Thylacine Mr Slee examined - in 1943 when he was 12 years old - also lacked stripes but was different from the first in that it was jet black. The young farmer found this animal dead in one of the many snares he set for kangaroos. It was 'large, sleek and shiny' and was black all over apart from a few flecks of white, which he assumed had grown over old scars.

Not knowing what to do with them, Mr Slee simply left both carcasses to rot in the bush. This may seem an odd thing to do but perhaps, back in the early 1940s, when it was generally assumed the Thylacine still existed in Tasmania, finding Thylacine-like animals on the mainland may not have seemed so strange as it would today. That these discoveries occurred during the momentous early years of World War II also may have tended to make them seem less important to Mr Slee, who was, after all, only a boy at the time.

Mr Slee believes the Thylacines have been building up in numbers since about the early 1970s and thinks they are responsible for the disappearance of the grey brush wallabies that previously thrived in the area. The animals also apparently prey on kangaroos. Over the years Mr Slee has found several killed and mutilated in a most distinctive manner: their heads had been torn off and completely devoured. His dogs, he says, can sense when the creatures are on the prowl: though they are not normally allowed indoors, on some nights they scurry inside, apparently scared witless.

Because Mr Slee claims such a large number of Thylacine sightings and because he can produce no absolutely indisputable physical evidence it is tempting to dismiss his stories altogether. To do so, however, would be foolish and unfair, because much of what he has said about the West Australian Thylacines - even the most improbable details - has been verified by other witnesses.

When describing the animals, several other eyewitnesses, such as June Maughan, who saw one near the mouth of the Margaret River, insisted the creatures, though Thylacine-like in every other detail, were definitely not striped.

Others, like Mrs N.F. Hemery of West Pingelly, have supported what Mr Slee says about the animal's gait. During a lengthy and very close encounter with a large and possibly quite old animal, Mrs Hemery and her two children noticed that 'the tail was shaped like a kangaroo and the hind legs moved like a kangaroo, the front legs like a galloping horse'.

Even what Mr Slee says about the Thylacine's predilection for headhunting has also been backed up by other witnesses. Tom Longbottom of Nannup, for instance, said Thylacines sometimes appear on his property and that '... now and again we find a lamb with its head eaten off. Just the head. Then we find 'roos with their heads gone as well'.

His claims about the behaviour of his dogs are also borne out by the testimony of several other people, including the Holland family of Busselton. After a series of Thylacine sightings around their farm they heard 'a blood curdling scream' one night.

'Our dog,' said Garry Holland, 'which is not allowed in the house, came grovelling in on his stomach. He seemed petrified with fright.'

In addition to this apparent vindication of his statements about colour, gait, diet and the behaviour of dogs, there are, in Mr Slee's testimony, one or two other elements that cause us to take him seriously. These are discussed in the conclusions chapter of Out of the Shadows.

Throughout the late 1970s Thylacine sightings continued to be reported throughout the south-west of the state, but the story did not develop in any significant way until, in the early 1980s, Kevin Cameron became involved in the mystery.

Mr Cameron, now in his late 40s, was employed for many years as a feral pig hunter by the Agriculture Protection Board and is, by all accounts, an exceptionally good, highly experienced bushman and tracker. He was called upon frequently by police and emergency services to assist in the search for drugs and for lost people and on one occasion saved the life of nine year old Edward Davies, missing for two days in cold, rainy conditions.

During his career with the A.P.B. he killed more than 1,300 wild pigs. Proud of his Aboriginal ancestry, he often set aside his rifle and did the job with a spear. In 1981 a badly injured right leg left him temporarily unemployed - and led him, inadvertently, into the hunt for the Thylacine.

Late in that year, for something to do, he checked out reports of Thylacine-like animals near Myalup. After finding blurred tracks, and some duck and kangaroo carcasses, he became badly infected with the 'Tiger bug'.

Thereafter, he visited the locations of many sightings. Sometimes, using a steel spear to support his injured knee, he scoured the bush alone; more often he directed operations from a vehicle, leaving the bush bashing to his sons Kevin and Shane and to his tracker dogs, Sam and Lobo.

On October 18, 1983 they experienced their first clear sighting when they surprised a Thylacine and drove to within ten metres of it on a remote forest track near Nannup.

'It reared up on its back legs,' said Mr Cameron 'and leapt forward to cross the road.' It had a large head, rounded ears, several stripes, and a long rigid tail. He released Lobo who chased it into the bush and bailed it up. As Mr Cameron hobbled after them he could see its head above the underbrush: 'it gave a series of cough-like sounds and seemed to be standing on its hind legs'. The animal made a successful break for freedom when it saw him approach. Mr Cameron and young Kevin later photographed two sets of tracks.

The most extraordinary feature of this incident is, of course, the claim that the

Thylacine is capable of rearing onto its hind legs and even of hopping like a kangaroo when hard pressed. As we mentioned in the first chapter, however, several colonial-era Tasmanians said the same thing about the Tasmanian tigers. Mr Cameron's observation is supported, also, by the testimony of at least one other West Australian witness, Garry Holland.

Mr Holland said that at 7.30am one sunny morning he was driving near his Busselton farm when 'I saw this animal resting on its hind legs like a kangaroo about 30 metres ahead of me. It watched me for about a minute before it disappeared into the forest. It had a mottled coat and stood about half a metre high. It had a strange sort of prancing gait.'

In 1982 Mr Cameron met Sid Slee and during the summer of 1982-83 they teamed up and made a sustained effort to collect tangible evidence. At Hillside, using sand traps and bait, Mr Cameron succeeded in making several very clear plaster casts of footprints. Some of them showed five toes and resembled the forepaws of a Thylacine and some that showed the four toes and distinctively long heel of the animal's back feet.

Several more headless kangaroos were also found and photographed. However, despite a great deal of spotlighting by night and bush-bashing by day - and one or two apparent near misses when their dogs got on the creatures' scent - the men did not succeed in filming the creatures.

They had no luck, either, with the traps painstakingly built by Mr Slee and his son Ian: they were sprung occasionally, but caught only foxes.

The Cameron Photos, 1984

After his efforts with the Slees in the Yoongarillup area, Kevin Cameron soldiered on alone. Finally, in early November 1984, while re-checking an area he had searched many times before, his luck changed: he spotted a Thylacine, and, before it became aware of him, began to stalk it, camera in hand.

'I got to within 10 metres of the animal,' he said, 'but it was so well camouflaged that if I hadn't been looking for it I could have passed without seeing it.'

The animal was so involved with what it was doing - digging into the base of a burnt-out Jarrah tree - that it wasn't aware of him until he had taken six photographs. Finally, however, 'The click of the camera disturbed it and it stopped digging to look at me squarely before it vanished into the surrounding vegetation'.

The two pictures that we have seen show the animal in two slightly different positions but in both only the hindquarters and the tail are clearly visible. The pelt is dark with broad stripes, which extend down the rear legs and a long tail projects stiffly out from the body, ending in what looks like a tuft of hair. After Mr Cameron showed the photos to Alex Harris of The West Australian and the story hit the headlines, there was a sudden surge of interest from previously sceptical scientists, some of who began to sound like born-again Thylacine believers.

Dr Anthony Burbidge, head of the Western Australian Wildlife Research Centre said the pictures were the best evidence yet produced for the existence of the mainland Thylacines. 'We are taking the sighting very seriously,' he said. Dr D. Kitchener, Curator of Mammals at the Museum of Western Australia, found them very interesting and thought they 'very much warranted further examination'. The WA Minister for Fisheries and Wildlife, Mr Evans, said this could be one of the wildlife events of the century and that if the creature were proven to be a Thylacine his government would immediately declare it an endangered species.

Believing they had great commercial value (he mentioned a figure of $53,000) Mr Cameron did not allow his photos to be used by any Australian newspapers. However, when Athol Douglas, a retired museum official, wrote an account of the WA Thylacine phenomenon for the British *New Scientist* magazine, Cameron reluctantly allowed him to use them.

When he examined the negative, Mr Douglas saw the film had been cut and that some frames were missing. He could see that the photographs had been taken from different angles, which made it 'impossible for the series to have been taken in 20 or 30 seconds, as Cameron had stated'.

Although Cameron had told him he was alone at the time, one negative showed the shadow of another person pointing what looked like a shotgun.

When the article was published, *New Scientist* readers quickly pointed out that shadows in two of the photos suggested they had not been taken at the same time. This idea gained strength when Mr Douglas later subjected the pictures to colour separation tests. From these tests he deduced the photographs had been taken not in 20 or 30 seconds, but over several hours.

Kevin Cameron would never tell Mr Douglas where the photographs were taken and he wouldn't respond to many other relevant questions. Despite this, interestingly enough, Mr Douglas still thought the pictures were of a real Thylacine. He thought one photograph - the one in which the shadow of the man with the shotgun is visible - was of a live creature. All the others, he believed, were taken several hours later of the same animal in a state of rigor mortis.

Mr Douglas hoped that, after a decent interval, the carcass would be 'found', 'shot by persons unknown'. That was perhaps wishful thinking; the hoped-for carcass was never surfaced.

Perhaps the most frustrating thing about Mr Cameron's story is that he claims that, on becoming aware of him, the creature '... stopped digging to look at me squarely before it vanished into the surrounding vegetation'.

Why, then, didn't he photograph its head?

One would also expect that, after the event, in order to establish the size of the animal, something of known dimensions - a rifle, a dog, a human being - would have been photographed next to the Jarra tree. If such comparison shots were taken they were not shown to Athol Douglas or to any other scientist. Mr Cameron's story, as reported, leaves many other questions unanswered (where, for instance, were his ever-present dogs on this occasion?), but one of its oddest elements is what the tiger-hunter says about his clothing. After spotting the animal, he said, 'To cut down the noise I peeled off my clothes and crawled through the undergrowth in my underpants'.

Mr Cameron's disrobing gave some newspaper editors an irresistible headline opportunity. ('HUNTER IN UNDERPANTS SNAPS WHAT MAY BE TASMANIAN TIGER' trumpeted the Sydney Morning Herald) but they did not question the logic of it.

To us, however, this detail seems strange to say the least. It could be seen as embroidery calculated to draw attention to Mr Cameron's Aboriginal ancestry or to add a little colour to the story.

We detect - as it were - four holes in the 'underpants' story. Firstly, disrobing would have consumed valuable time; secondly, doing so would result in little if any reduction in noise; thirdly, while Rambo may run through the jungle bare-chested, in real life few hunters who have the option of clothes deliberately crawl through the undergrowth naked. Finally, during his time with the Slees, Mr Cameron often dressed from top to toe in camouflage fatigues. Such an outfit - or any ordinary bush gear - would be, we imagine, much less conspicuous than Mr Cameron's pale skin: despite his Aboriginal ancestry he has the appearance and colouration of a European. There are, on the other hand, some positive aspects to the story. Mr Cameron, unemployed and short of money, could have sold the pictures to any Australian tabloid. Instead, he chose to send them, gratis, to *New Scientist*, whose sophisticated readers, he knew, would subject them to microscopic examination and sceptical appraisal.

If there really are Thylacines in Western Australia, Mr Cameron, by all accounts a courageous and exceptionally gifted hunter and tracker, would be just the kind of man to find them.

Naturally, we would like to believe the Cameron photographs are genuine. Since 1985, however, Kevin Cameron has become almost as hard to track down as the

Thylacine itself. We haven't managed to get his side of the story or permission to use the photographs.

As the years go by, it seems less and less likely the object in the Cameron photographs is a Thylacine, dead or alive, at all. That, however, does not necessarily mean the entire West Australian Thylacine phenomenon is an illusion. Since the photos were taken in 1984 people have continued, intermittently and in the same general areas as before, to report encounters with large, striped, dog-like animals: the mystery goes on.

Mainland Thylacines - Conclusions

As mentioned earlier, the nearest thing to hard evidence is the Thylacine humerus (shoulder bone) found in northwest WA in 1970 by Dr Michael Archer and colleagues.

This bone was found in a cave too small for human habitation and was surrounded by the crushed bones of many smaller animals. Since there was no trace of any other large predator, it seemed logical to assume the Thylacine had occupied the shelter for some time and had killed at least some of the smaller animals.

Because the broken Thylacine humerus was not large and would be destroyed in the process, it was not put through the radiocarbon dating process. A sample of the other bones, however, was analysed and the scientists were surprised to find the material tested out at less than 80 years old. The dating of these bones has never been challenged.

Dr Archer is careful to note that 'it is possible the age of the Thylacine bone differs from the age of the bone in the sample' but we find it difficult to see how the bone could be 3,000 years older than material lying right beside it in a tiny cave.

Dr Archer, in fact, accepts the possibility of the humerus being only 80 years old. He points out that there is reason to suspect Thylacines may have lingered on in the Kimberleys longer than in most parts of the mainland. This is because the dingo - the Thylacine's great competitor – didn't seem to impact the area as heavily or as early as most other parts of the continent. Mr Archer is also aware of the numerous eyewitness reports of Thylacine-like creatures, which have come from the Kimberleys in the modern era.

Although Dr Archer's Thylacine humerus represents the closest thing yet to concrete evidence of the mainland Thylacine's survival, there is, just possibly, one other piece of hard evidence.

In the introduction to this chapter we used the story of the mummified Mundrabilla Thylacine carcass to illustrate in a dramatic way the fact that Thylacines really did inhabit mainland Australia thousands of years ago. Since writing those lines, however, we have become aware of a startling theory put forward by Athol Douglas, the scientist already mentioned in relation to the Cameron photographs.

Mr Douglas, formerly a Senior Experimental Officer at the Western Australian Museum, maintains that far from being 4,600 years old when discovered in 1966, the carcass may have been only one year old.

On examining the carcass just after it was found, Mr Douglas decided immediately it was very recent. It was '... fully covered with hair, had a musty odour, and looked like a recent dried-out carcass after the maggots had left but before the hide-and-fur-eating invertebrates had begun their attack. It was not a dehydrated carcass with dried intestines and flesh.'

When the carcass was carbon dated at 4,600 years, Mr Douglas reluctantly accepted the finding, although he was aware that dry tissues, not bone, were used in the dating. Later he re-examined the carcass and became convinced his initial opinion was correct.

He is adamant that the animal is not dried and mummified as claimed. He points out that Jacoba and David Lowry, who found the carcass, said at the time that 'The soft tissue had decomposed to a tarry substance which coated the exposed bones ... However, the tongue and left eyeball were still recognisable, and a musty odour of decomposition was noticeable ... [rats] ... appeared also to have chewed the abdomen ... [rat] faeces were scattered around the carcass.'.

Mr Douglas believes the tarry substance is dried adipocere, 'grave wax, which he has seen many times on recent carcasses found in caves and mine shafts. During a 1986 visit to 'Thylacine Hole', Mr Douglas established that the rocks on which the carcass was lying were a very recent fall from the cave roof. He also found a dingo carcass, which, since it was not present in 1966, was less than 20 years old. The dingo carcass, hairless, dry and odourless, is in a far worse state or preservation than the supposedly 4,600 year old Thylacine.

Mr Douglas points out that although the bulk of modern WA Thylacine reports come from the southwest of the state, some have come from Mundrabilla Station and the surrounding area.

We also have a report - now lost somewhere in our files - of a young couple on a motorbike almost colliding with a Thylacine on the Nullarbor in the vicinity of Mundrabilla.

The Thylacine remains may or may not prove to be recent but there are other pieces of evidence, which, though perhaps not rock hard', are nevertheless a bit more tangible than mere eyewitness testimony:

Footprints

Given the large number of sighting reports, remarkably few plaster casts or photographs of tracks have been collected. There could be four reasons for this:

(a) A Thylacine's footprints do not, to the average person, appear radically different to those of a dog and may not therefore attract the eye. A Thylacine's tracks are also not spectacularly huge: no bigger than those of a medium to large dog.

(b) In the late 20th century most city people - and most country folk as well - are very poor trackers.

(c) Animal tracks are notoriously difficult to photograph clearly.

(d) Plaster of Paris is not a substance usually kept close at hand - and for various reasons casts of tracks are not always easy to make.

We have yet to see a photo of alleged Thylacine tracks - in situ - that is clear enough to be of any use. Some sketches of tracks are a little better as evidence: the one by Mrs Anderson, for instance, appears to show the long heel characteristic of the Thylacine's rear foot, but most are of little real value.

Mrs Anderson and two or three other people in South Australia and Victoria have made plaster casts of tracks over the years. Most of these have apparently not been particularly clear, but some casts displayed recently by the Rare Fauna Research Society do seem very similar to pre-1936 sketches of Tasmanian Tiger tracks.

The clearest casts of all are those produced by Kevin Cameron at Sid Slee's Hillside property. These casts are so perfectly well defined that - providing they are genuine - they come near to proving Thylacines exist in the west.

If the casts seem a little too good, it should be remembered that Mr Cameron was a professional hunter and tracker. He obtained the casts by setting up (in an area where Thylacines had often been reported) several areas of raked sand baited with freshly killed rabbits.

Photographs

As mentioned above, the creature in the Cameron photographs closely resembles a Thylacine. Unfortunately, however, serious doubts have been raised as to the validity of the pictures.

We have some serious doubts, also, about the 1964 Rilla Martin photograph.

The type of camera and film she used, the distance between her and the animal, the time of day and whether or not she was alone are all unknown. The absence of comparison shots taken at the same site is frustrating, as is Miss Martin's absolute refusal, since the late 1960s, to be interviewed.

E.H.M. Ealey of the Monash University Zoology Department, who took a considerable interest in the Ozenkadnook Tiger in the 1960s, did not think much of the photograph.

In 1969 he wrote to researcher Keith Zeinert:

> Miss Martin saw something dash away through the scrub, pointed her camera at it and exposed some film. She gave the film to her cousin to develop and it was not returned to her until some seven months later, showing this remarkable beast ... as the cousin ... is known for his practical jokes, it is thought that he constructed a dummy tiger, photographed it, and placed it amongst Miss Martin's negatives in place of the picture she took, which must have only shown a blur anyway.

Much of what Mr Earley said sharply contradicts the story that accompanied the photograph when it was first published in the *Wimmera Mail Times* in September 1964. Although he sounds sure of his facts, it is probably impossible at this late stage to establish the real truth of the matter.

We feel, on the balance of the evidence - such as it is - that the 'Tiger' in the photograph probably is a cutout or model - but there are some intriguing things about it which sometimes tempt us to change our minds.

The 'Ozenkadnook Tiger 'was widely believed to be a Thylacine. If a person were intent on staging a hoax, he or she would surely have made a cutout or model that closely resembled that animal. Instead, the creature in the photograph, while Thylacine-like in some respects, is not exactly like a Tasmanian tiger. Its stripe pattern is different, the head and neck do not look quite right and the general bearing of the animal looks somehow different.

However, while the stripes on the Martin animal - which start at the neck rather than the shoulders - do not match those of Tasmanian Thylacines, they do match some mainland eyewitness testimony and sketches.

It may be worth pointing out, also that a sketch done by South Australian eyewitness Don Gillette in 1968 shows an animal whose stance and general appearance are strikingly similar to the creature in the photo.

There is a third photograph - in fact a 8mm movie film - which might show a mainland Thylacine. The value of the 'Anderson film', however, depends more on the high quality of the witnesses than on the clarity of the images it shows.

Archie Anderson was a WA police officer and a keen, very experienced wildlife photographer. Wildlife lovers regarded his wife Iris as a virtual patron saint of the state's wildlife. She and Archie kept a sanctuary for injured and neglected animals at their Bicton home. One day in 1969 Mr and Mrs Anderson, accompanied by Mr and Mrs Robert Moore and their daughter, were driving a few miles south of Carnarvon when they passed a strange-looking animal about 15 feet off the road.

'The idea was to back the car slowly so as not to frighten it,' said Mr Anderson. This was accomplished; they all had a clear, if brief, view of the animal and were nearly certain it had stripes. It looked thin and hungry, its tail was stiff and thick and it had big ears thickly made. It looked, they said, more like a hyena than anything.

As they stopped and reached for their cameras the creature moved. 'All I could do,' said Archie, 'was press the button on my camera as the animal moved off.' The gait had a peculiar cantering motion.

The six-second film clip is not particularly clear. Archie apparently didn't have time to focus properly and when he began shooting the creature was about 60 metres away.

As it appears on the film, the animal does not seem to be very large. The tail does not really appear to be as thick as described and is not held out rigidly. The legs appear to be longer in proportion to the body than a Thylacine's and the lower rear leg doesn't look quite right. All these features, though, could have been distorted by bad focus and heat shimmer.

On the positive side, the creature's head and the heavy upper hindquarters, out to the butt of the tail could be those of a Thylacine.

Wildlife expert Ian Offer said the film was 'the best recorded evidence that the tiger exists in WA. No normal animal can run in that manner. The way it loped along with its back legs and front legs not coordinated indicated it was a marsupial'.

A Western Australian Museum officer, Duncan Merrilees, was not so sure. 'Its gait,' he said, 'seemed abnormal but not impossible for a dog or fox. Its tail was long and held curved, in length consistent with fox, in curvature with dog. The identity of the animal seemed to me uncertain, with dog, fox or Thylacine as possibilities.'

The Anderson film is certainly of interest as a cryptozoological artefact but it doesn't really prove anything. The animal depicted could be a mangy fox. A large fox whose body and normally distinctively bushy tail have been stripped can look rather alien.

On the other hand, of course, the Andersons, as highly experienced observers of wildlife, had probably seen mangy foxes before.

Animal kills

Several of the kangaroo carcasses found in West Australian Thylacine hot-spots really do appear to have been killed and mauled in a unique manner: their heads have been torn right off their shoulders and either carried away or eaten whole.

Sceptics, of course, may point out that Tasmanian Thylacines were not noted for headhunting. They might also ask why the supposed mainland Thylacines have not engaged in the wholesale slaughter of sheep, which was attributed to the Tasmanian variety.

The above constitutes all that could be seen as reasonably 'hard' evidence supporting the existence of the mainland tigers. There are also, however, certain recurring patterns in the testimonial evidence that are worth looking at.

Movement

As we have already discussed - in relation to Mr Slee's evidence - many witnesses have mentioned the way Thylacines sometimes move their back legs in unison, as a kangaroo does. Just as interesting are a few reports that refer to vaguely horse-like movements by the creatures. As mentioned earlier, Archie and Iris Anderson said the gait of the creature they filmed had 'a peculiar cantering effect'. The following excerpts from the statements of other eyewitnesses contain similar details:

1. Mrs Hemery, West Pingelly, WA: '... the hind legs moved like a kangaroo, the front legs like a galloping horse.'

2. Bob Rethus, Brimpaen, Victoria: '... the head sat up almost vertical to its body as it ran, something like a horse when it arches its neck.'

Surely if someone was hoaxing or hallucinating a Thylacine sighting, horse-like imagery would not be in the forefront of their mind. However, interestingly enough, such imagery has been used on at least one occasion in Tasmania itself.

In 1970 D. Whayman told Eric Guiler of seeing a Thylacine, which moved 'like a trotting horse'.

In the light of these statements it is interesting to look again at the creature in the Rilla Martin photo. The carriage of its head is rather equine: it is held high, rather like that of a trotting horse.

Pelt markings

Most mainland sightings appear to be of animals whose markings more or less match the stripe pattern of the Tasmanian Thylacines. As we have seen, however, some mainland witnesses describe Thylacines with considerably more stripes than the

Tasmanian tigers and others tell of seeing Thylacines with no stripes at all. Attempting to draw conclusions from this may seem foolish but it may be worth pointing out the following:

(a) The number and distribution of stripes varied a little on the Tasmanian tigers themselves: some had as few as 13 stripes and others as many as 22. Beneath the stripes, the basic colour of Tasmanian tigers also varied somewhat: from grey to golden brown.

(b) A 6000-year-old rock painting of a Thylacine in Arnhem Land, NT, shows the stripes starting at the neck and covering the entire body - similar to the markings on the animal in the Rilla Martin photo. (On the other hand, the stripe pattern on 'Old Hairy' the mummified Thylacine found near Eucla, WA, is not noticeably different to that of 'ordinary' Tasmanian tigers).

Behaviour

In the early days in Tasmania it was established that the Thylacines hunted alone, occasionally in pairs but never in packs. Since very few Australians have any knowledge of the Tasmanian tigers' habits, we feel it is quite significant that among mainland Thylacine witnesses exactly the same pattern has emerged. Almost all reports are of single animals, a small number refer to pairs and reports of three or more animals are extremely rare.

Although many of the preceding considerations give us hope that Thylacines may exist on the mainland the fact remains that (with the possible exception of the bone discovered by Mr Archer) not a single piece of hard evidence has been brought in for examination.

The next most powerful single argument against the existence of mainland Thylacines is this: there is no tradition concerning these creatures among mainland Aborigines. Since the collective folk memory of some Aboriginal groups has been shown to extend as far back as 3000 years the mainland Thylacines, however rare, should have rated at least a few casual references in folk tales.

The absence of Aboriginal Thylacine stories could be explained in this way: the Thylacines seen on the mainland are not descendants of the HelioThylacine at all, but are the descendants of Thylacines brought from Tasmania and released prior to 1936. This scenario is possibly the best single explanation for the mainland Thylacine reports.

But while the 'feral Tassie tiger' theory answers many questions it raises several others. The offspring of a pair of Thylacines released in southern Victoria in say, 1880, might possibly have spread throughout south-eastern Australia, but what about Western Australia, isolated from the east by thousands of kilometres of desert? Was another pair released there? And what of the stripeless and all-black Thylacines? Were the witnesses who reported these variations mistaken or lying?

Two odd incidents which occurred in Victoria could be seen as support, of a kind, for the Tasmanian tigers released-on-the-mainland theory: on two separate occasions Tasmanian devils - which are also supposed to have become extinct on the mainland thousands of years ago - have been discovered in Victoria. One was trapped at Tooborac in 1912 and two others were run over in April 1991 near Harcourt.

The existence of a few Tasmanian devils in Victoria, while interesting, does not, of course, prove anything about mainland Thylacines. Firstly, unlike the Thylacine, the devil is not extinct in Tasmania - it has until recent times thrived there. A few animals could, therefore have been brought to the mainland by private individuals at any time from 1803 to the present. Secondly, devils - only about the size of a large house cat - would have been a great deal easier to catch and transport than Thylacines. While the true age of the Mundrabilla carcass and the Kimberleys Thylacine humerus are still in doubt, it would be very rash to declare that mainland Thylacines still exist. The 'soft' - mainly testimonial - evidence, however, is so plentiful, so consistent and has come from so many areas over so many decades that it would be equally rash to say they did not.

~~~

*Tony Healy and Paul Cropper have investigated all manner of strange phenomena, both in Australia and overseas, since the mid-1970s. They have collaborated on many projects, notably in co-authoring **Out of the Shadows: Mystery Animals of Australia**, and **The Yowie**. Their latest book, **Australian Poltergeist**, explores Australia's rich history of 'noisy ghost' cases.*

*This chapter originally appeared in **Out of the Shadows: Mystery Animals of Australia** and has been reprinted here with the kind permission of the authors.*

References

1. The Advertiser 22 Nov 1960

2. The Border Watch, Mt Gambier, 31 July 1971

3. Douglas, A., "The Thylacine on Mainland Australia", Cryptozoology, 1990.

4. Naracoorte Herald 7 June 1974

5. Naracoorte News 17 Jan 1968

6. Mrs Parker's files

7. The Portland Observer July 1971; Dec 27, 1974

8. Sydney Morning Herald 8 Dec 1962

9. Walkabout June 1968

10. Wildlife, November 1947

11. Wimmera Mail Times 6 & 9 Aug 1962; 7 Feb 1966; 29 July 1966; 1 Feb 1967; 9 Aug 1967; 6 Oct 1967

12. Archer, M. "New Information about the Quaternary distribution of the Thylacine (marsupialia, Thylacinidae) in Australia. Journal of the Royal Society of Western Australia, 57(2) 1974.

13. Carmody, Freda, letter to Mrs Dawn Anderson 20 November 1973

14. Daily News 11 Nov 1970

15. Longbottom, Tom, letter to Sid Slee, p 37 The Haunt of the Marsupial Wolf

16. The New Scientist, 24 April 1985.

17. Merilees, Duncan, WA Museum file note, 2 Oct 1972.

18. News of the North, 18 Nov 1970

19. Slee, S. The Haunt of the Marsupial Wolf

20. The Sun 26 Oct 1970

21. The Sunday Times 6 Dec 1970 and 29 Oct 1972

22. Sydney Morning Herald 17 Nov 1984

23. Walsh, G. Australia's Great Rock Art

24. The West Australian 16 & 23 Jan 1984; 28 May 1984; 16 & 17 Nov 1984; 19 Oct 1970

THE TASMANIAN ZEBRA-WOLF.

An American artist's depiction of the Thylacine, which was described historically as the 'Tasmanian Zebra-Wolf'. *Courtesy San Francisco Chronicle, 1896.*

CHAPTER 5

Thylacine Sightings Outside Tasmania
by Malcolm Smith

I have been following reports of Australian mystery animals for several decades, but the ones I find most perplexing concern Thylacines on the mainland. All over the mainland, fossils and Aboriginal artwork confirm their former presence, but they all went extinct 3,500 years ago. Or did they? For his book, *The Last Tasmanian Tiger*, Dr Robert Paddle meticulously researched the 19th century accounts, and found some from a naturalist called 'Cambrian', who examined the skin of one killed in the Blue Mountains, west of Sydney, and another apparently from the Lake Torrens/Flinders Ranges area of South Australia. He also unearthed a lecture by a prominent scientist, Dr John Litchfield, referring to their current existence in South Australia. There were also Aboriginal traditions of their survival in the Flinders Ranges until approximately the 1830s[1].

Incidentally, he also cited 19th century documentation of Tasmanian *devils* in Victoria, as well as five separate specimens taken from that State between 1912 and 1991. Concerning this, he makes the pointed observation:

> 'There would have to be a phenomenally high population of incompetent Victorian naturalists illegally keeping Tasmanian devils as pets, in order for as many as five to become museum specimens[2].'

Be that as it may, the presence of small, remnant populations in the recent past would be difficult to explain all their alleged appearances at the present day. There exists a sort of 'Thylacine Fever' in some quarters, which results in any anomalous bush predator being labelled a Thylacine – if not by the witness, then by the journalist reporting it.

---

1   Paddle, Robert, 2000. *The Last Tasmanian Tiger: The history and extinction of the Thylacine.* Cambridge University Press, pp 22 - 23

2   Paddle *ibid* p 25

Approximately three per cent of the dingo population is brindle hybrids i.e. they are dingo-dog crosses, with broken, stripe-like markings, often covering the whole body. And, as Dr Corbett explained:

> 'In Victoria sightings of similarly coloured animals sometimes give rise to the forlorn hope that Thylacines still exist in the bush.'[3]

Add to this is the presence of mange, producing anomalous blotching and markings, and removing the brush of the dingo or feral dog's tail, and the opportunity for misidentification is enormous. A dog-like animal should never be identified as a Thylacine unless it is seen close up to bear a row of dark, vertical, *unbroken* stripes from chest to tail, and hindquarters which, like a kangaroo's, taper into a thick, kangaroo-like tail. A Thylacine's tail was not as inflexible as has often been portrayed, but any tail that curls over the back, or is fluffy or brushy, is not attached to a Thylacine.

All this having been said, the number of noteworthy mainland reports are far too numerous for an article of this size. I will be forced to provide just a tiny selection. Although these are some of the best, it is important to remember they are just the tip of the iceberg. And if even one is correct ...

Victoria

South Gippsland must be quite an interesting place, if local folklore is accurate, for it contains black panthers, pumas, *and* Thylacines. Take, for example, what happened to a young couple in November 1988, and which was apparently reported to the Rare Fauna Research Society shortly afterwards.[4]

Just after dark, as they were driving down an unsealed road, a striped animal larger than a fox crossed the road from an adjacent paddock and ran up another dirt road. 'Fox!' cried the young woman – but she knew it couldn't be a fox, for the back part was mostly stripes; they stood out in the headlights, black against a fawny background. However, her companion remembered the stripes being white on a dark background. This is not as paradoxical as it might appear, if you consider whether a

---

3   Corbett, Laurie, 1995. *The Dingo in Australia and Asia.* University of NSW Press, plate 8

4   Tobin, Mary, 1990. 'More Tasmanian tiger news?' *Foster Mirror*, 3 October 1990

zebra is a white horse with black stripes, or a black horse with white stripes. It means the stripes were solid and close together – just what you would *not* expect from a brindled dingo hybrid. It also means that the witnesses' memories were not overly cross-contaminated. They also both remembered a long, thin tail, like a greyhound's. The gait was also unusual.

This occurred in a 'hotspot' of many similar sightings, perhaps of the same individual, perhaps not. One person living about 10 km away happened to see, at dusk sometime between November 1987 and January 1988, a striped animal casually walk across his unfenced front lawn. Much to his amazement, two smaller individuals, otherwise identical to the first, came and joined it. He assumed they were cubs, and suspected that it had come to drink from a container near his fishpond, as foxes often did. They were so close, he could have counted the stripes. His neighbour two doors down scoffed at the story until, a few months later, the same animal trotted past his own property[5].

Let's also look at the experience of Fred Silvester, a former assistant police commissioner, and his wife in 1997.

A trained observer aware of how inaccurate some witnesses can be, he was openly sceptical about reported 'tiger' sightings by several other Loch Sport residents. That is until 9 am on 1 February, when he saw a strange animal standing at the fishpond in his garden in Seagull Drive, which abuts bush. He alerted his wife; both moved to a verandah about 10 metres from the animal:

> It was a browny colour, about the size of a medium-sized dog, with a thick tail that came to a point, and dark stripes that went right to the butt of the tail. We stood for about 30 seconds, then it looked up at me, turned around and loped off. Its action was peculiar. I have never seen a Tasmanian tiger, but I used to shoot a lot, and I've seen a lot of mangy old foxes, and it wasn't that.

Mrs Silvester described the stripes as 'reddy tan', starting behind the shoulders and running to the butt of the tail, which she estimated was 10 centimetres wide at that point, and tapering like a wallaby's. 'It had a long head, a bit like an Alsatian, with ears that were standing up, not floppy.'[6]You can't get much better testimony than

---

5   Tobin, *op. cit.*

6   Rule, Andrew, 1997. 'Australia: Agenda – Tiger Tales – It' out there somewhere ... or is it?' *Sunday Age* (Melbourne) 1st June 1997

that. The journalist who recorded it, Andrew Rule, also reported a large number of other sightings, with the same meticulous attention to detail. In addition, he also spoke to 74-year-old John Anderson, a former soil scientist and farmer, and to his daughter, Anne, about what they experienced in the late 1970s. His property was located in a coastal grazing area between Sale and Seaspray, and that day he set out with his kelpie and his .22 rifle to check stock, fences, and water. As he went about his business, what he initially mistook for a wallaby loped away on all fours about 20 metres from where he stood:

> It had a peculiar gait, not like a dog. The tail was thickish at the butt. There were marking on the hindquarters. It was coloured in autumn tones: the body was rusty brown and the stripes were dark brown from the loin backwards. It was every bit as big as a Kelpie.[7]

He could have shot it then and there − and perhaps solved a cryptozoological mystery − but he decided not to, because he had no idea what the creature was. When he arrived back at the house, Anne, then aged 16, was already there. She had set off in the opposite direction to her father, and had been chasing rabbits with her border collie, Devil, when what was apparently the same animal ran out of the tea trees. It was a bit bigger than the dog, a brown tan colour, with darker markings around it, starting in mid-loin and going back to the tail, and it had an unusual gait. Devil chased it to within 15 feet of her, at which point it spun around to face him, and she noted its 'short, triangular, thick sort of ears, not really like a dog'.

'The dog ran towards him. The animal's muzzle stayed straight. That is, the top didn't move, but he dropped his bottom jaw right down ... like a medieval drawbridge over a moat.' She mimes this, holding one hand flat, dropping the other down through more than 90 degrees to form a gaping 'mouth'. 'Then,' she continues, leaning forward in her chair, reliving the moment, 'he made this really bizarre sound. It was a weird 'yip, yip!' from the bottom of the throat. The hairs went up on the back of my neck. I was terrified. So was my dog. He turned around and bolted. I was left standing with nothing but a stick. I ran all the way home to tell Mum, but the dog beat me.'

Back home, they consulted a book on Australian mammals, and she recognised it as a Tasmanian tiger.

---

7   Rule *op. cit.*

Normally, I would have reservations about sightings reported 20 years after the event. There is too much time for the memory to be contaminated. But here we have two independent sightings in broad daylight at very close range. What particularly impressed me was the reaction of the animal to the dog. While I cannot confirm, with absolute certainty the vocalisation was that of a Thylacine, it obviously wasn't that of a dog. More to the point, the Thylacine's jaws were known to have an extremely wide gape, and it was known to display this gape as a threat posture. This also becomes relevant in the next account.

Queensland

Roy Swaby, a 58-year-old retired marine engineer, lived south of Woodgate, in southeast Queensland, but if what he experienced on the evening of 8 August, 1995 had happened in Tasmania, there would certainly have been zoologists and rangers swarming over the site. He didn't inform the press for another three weeks[8], during a 'flap' of anomalous animal sightings. When I interviewed him by telephone five days later, he was still obviously overwhelmed by the experience[9].

He had gone out to buy a couple of cigars and, since he and his wife were both authorised wildlife carers and always on the lookout for injured wildlife, he had his 100 watt halogen spotlights on as well as his headlights. Returning home through an area of about 100 km² of dense wallum, he was alerted by a grey kangaroo leaping across the road in front of him. Suddenly, a huge striped predator hurled itself onto the road, clearing 15 feet in one jump. He had just been changing gears at the time, so he put the vehicle into neutral and simply coasted. The animal would have been about 50 or 60 metres from him at first, and 20 metres when it left, and the sighting lasted 15 - 20 seconds. When it saw him, it sat back on its hindquarters, with its forepaws off the ground, and made a sound that was difficult to hear above the engine noise, and gave a gape threat. It sprang like a cat, not a kangaroo, and was very graceful in its movements, its body rippling like a cheetah's.

His impression was as if someone had joined half a dingo to half a kangaroo. He could even see its whiskers. Its eyes glowed yellow-green in the light; 15-20 dark, vertical stripes decorated its sandy coloured body from near the shoulder to the root

---

8   McRae, Toni (1995). 'Buderim beast' makes man shake. *The Sunday Mail* (Brisbane) 27 August 1995.

9   Smith, Malcolm (1996). *Bunyips and Bigfoots: In Search of Australia's Mystery Animals*. Millennium Books, pp 107-8.

of its tapering tail. He estimated its length as four to five feet, with the tail an extra two to three feet. But what he had difficulty putting into words was the way its jaws gaped. It was like a crocodile, like a snake, like a mantrap, about 160° (almost certainly an overestimate). Its face disappeared when the jaws were opened. I don't believe in asking leading questions, so it was only after I had elicited this information that I referred him to the Thylacine gape threat.

His face was white when he arrived home. A quarter of an hour later, he called together a couple of witnesses, and made a sketch, although he later told me the hindquarters were actually higher. Next day, he found footprints 120 mm by 100 mm, but the photograph wasn't good enough for identification. Then he went to the library for a book on Australian mammals, and identified it as a Thylacine. If his description and sketch are accurate, that is all it could be. If his estimate of the dimensions was correct, it was also oversized. The three skins I measured at the Australian Museum averaged 3foot 5 inches [1041mm] head and body length, and the tails 18½ inches [470mm]. As far as I can ascertain, the largest ever measured – which was also the first to be described – was 4 foot 6 inches [1390 mm] head and body, with a 20 inch [508mm] tail[10].

This story has a couple of sequels. About 6.30am on Sunday, 11 May, 1997, Jim Wieland, who had just been checking some crab pots, was driving through Woodgate National Park when he saw a strange animal by the side of the road. He called the ranger, who called Mr Swaby, who called me, and I was able to interview the witness by phone about nine hours after the event.

The sighting lasted only four or five seconds, at a distance of 20 or 40 metres. It was about as big as a good-sized cattle dog, darker than a fox, with darker stripes on the rear part. They were not prominent, but definitely present. He was a little vague about the details; he thought they extended vertically only half the height of the animal, and were present only on the rear. It had a thick chest and very heavy back legs. The hindquarters tapered into the tail like a kangaroo's. The tail was very long, even as long as the body. It did not run away like a fox, but bounded in a clumsy fashion like a horse or kangaroo.

I am not at all convinced this was a genuine Thylacine, but it is worth noting that it

10   Smith, Malcolm (1982). 'Review of the Thylacine (Marsupialia, Thylacinidae)' pp 237 – 253 in *Carnivorous Marsupials*, vol. 1, Michael Archer (ed), Roy. Zool. Soc. NSW.

was seen only four or five miles from Mr Swaby's original encounter. Secondly, one of Mr Swaby's acquaintances, Henry Seery, had never seen a picture of a Tasmanian tiger until he watched a TV documentary in the early 1990s, at which point he told his family: 'They're not extinct. If you want to go up to Eurimbula you'll find plenty.'

This was 90km north of Bundaberg, but in the 1970s he and his mates used to shoot wallabies for crab bait in the area, before it became a national park. He was used to shooting foxes, dingoes, and feral cats, but he never used to shoot the striped 'dogs' he encountered there, because he assumed they were special dogs belonging to a local grazier. He would see them through his 39 x 40 variable telescopic sights at 120 metres while spotlighting.

Seery would see their tracks, which made his Alsatians' paw prints look like those of puppies. They had bigger, rounder prints, and the claws didn't retract like a dog's *(sic)*. He estimated they were two metres to 2.3 metres from the tip of the straight tail to the snout, with chocolate stripes on the hindquarters. The legs were curvy and sort of came under the body rather than sticking back like that of a dog. It had a swaggering lope, and massive jaws. He saw one yawn, and you'd think the jaws were unhinged to see them open right up to the ear.[11]

It occurs to me that, whatever they were, if Mr Seery could regularly see them while spotlighting, then so could field zoologists. It might be worth their while to investigate.

New Guinea

New Guinea is a special case. It is part of the Australian biotic zone, inhabited by marsupials. The Thylacine is known to have existed there in the past,[12] its extinction being blamed on the same cause as in Australia: the introduction of the dingo, known over there as the New Guinea singing dog. Nevertheless, the island has been little explored zoologically, and it remains a labyrinth of mountains and valleys isolated from one another as 'ecological islands'. Virtually every zoological expedition turns up new species - admittedly usually of smaller size - but if any place outside of

---

11   Whittaker, Mark (1997). 'Look! There's one!' *The Australian Magazine*, pp 12 -18, insert of *The Weekend Australian*, 15-16 November 1997

12   Van Deusen, H. 1963. 'First New Guinea record of *Thylacinus.'Journal of Mammalogy* 44, pp 279 - 280

Tasmania hides a remnant population of Thylacines, it would be here. Ned Terry is a retired Tasmanian grazier, and an indefatigable Thylacine hunter. One October, probably in 1990, he received a phone call from a stranger living nearby – a neighbour who had spent 17 years as a missionary in the western half of the island controlled by Indonesia. Apparently, a colleague of his had screened a film about Australian animals in a remote highland area, and the natives went wild over the Thylacine, which they knew as a *dobsegna* living in the surrounding mountains. Mr Terry then contacted a missionary in the area, and obtained the following description:

> Head and shoulders like white man's dog, but with strong mouth. Tail is long and thin, almost the same length as the body. From ribs to hips, they have no intestines, meaning they are very thin in that area, and that part has stripes.[13]

Mr Terry thereupon called on his cousin, Robin, and together they went to the site. He found the natives knew a lot about the animal's biology, and lived in superstitious dread of it. He and Robin were unable to locate any specimen.

Mr Terry provided no evidence to back up his account, nor did he give the location of the animal, or explain how he obtained a permit to enter the interior of the Indonesian zone. (Perhaps the missionary pulled a few strings.) At the same time, there is nothing to refute the story, and it is not the only report of Thylacines from that part of the world.

On 25 March 1997, a statement came from Jos Buce Wenas, the Regent Head of District Level II, Jayawijaya, the central mountain range of Indonesian New Guinea located next to the Papua New Guinea border. He telephoned a local newspaper and announced that local missionaries had told him of a species of tiger a metre high in the regions of the Kurima Tableland, Oksibil and Okbibab, where it lived in caves, emerging at night to hunt the natives' livestock in packs[14]. Obviously, the story had gained a bit in the telling - either that, or the animals are not Thylacines. Thylacines

---

13   de Salis, Simon. 'The Tassie tiger is alive & well and living in New Guinea!' *People* (date not recorded, probably 1991)

14   'Pemangsa Mirip "Tasmania tiger" ditemukan di pedalaman Jayawijaya". *Suara Pembaruan* 25 March 1997

http://suarapembaruan.com/News/1997/03/250397/Headline/head05/head05.html(last accessed 20 May 1997, now a dead link) were not a metre high, and they hunt(ed) in small family groups, not large packs. However, it does appear that some mysterious predator inhabits this remote area, and it is far more likely to be a Thylacine than some completely unknown marsupial predator.

Once the English language press started picking up fragments of the story, a number of British animal lovers organised trips to the area. The Jakarta representative of the Worldwide Fund for Nature, Rom Liley, was quoted as saying:

> A Tasmanian tiger was caught near the Jayawijaya glacier in 1933 and transferred to Bonaris National Park in Tasmania, where it died three years later.[15]

This, of course, is total nonsense – even if the Beaumaris Zoo, the former name of Hobart Zoo, is intended for 'Bonaris National Park'. However, Mr Liley did say that he believed that Thylacines still existed in Jayawijaya, because residents of the Baliem Valley had recently reported wolf attacks on their cattle, so I suspect that was the site intended by Mr Terry, for it does tend to be open to tourists.

In 2000, an Austrian gentleman who had visited the Indonesian controlled part of New Guinea three times to satisfy an amateur interest in tribal culture, flora and fauna, told me that he always carries pictures of presumed native animals with him. On his most recent trip, there had been no questions about Thylacines, but the natives recognised it from a stamp carried by an Australian miner.

When I provided a translation of the original Indonesian articles on my website[16], it inspired a number of comments. Chad Arment, an American cryptozoologist, said: 'Some time in the mid to late-1990s, I was contacted by an exotic animal importer from Florida, who had collected reports of a Thylacine-like animal from New Guinea. (I don't unfortunately recall the exact location.) He was primarily over there purchasing snakes and other reptiles that had been captured, for export to the U.S. While over there, he was told about a strange dog-like animal that was consistent with a Thylacine. He came back, hoping to find someone willing to invest in an expedition

---

15   Vignes, Spencer (1997) 'Indonesia: British animal lovers rush to Irian Jaya.' *Southeast Asia Jakarta Post* 1st June 1997

16   Smith, Malcolm 2011. 'Thylacines in Indonesian New Guinea?' http://malcolmscryptids.blogspot.com.au/2011/10/Thylacines-in-indonesian-new-guinea.html

to look for it, but I never heard whether he was able to do so.' Also, in January 2013, an anonymous reader commented: 'I have actually seen one in Jayawijaya myself when I was stationed there for three years! The colour is grey, unlike the Tasmanian species. Could be a new species. Unfortunately, I did not take photos. I did not expect I would see one ... alive!'

Finally, and most recently, Dr Karl Shuker has provided the following information[17]:

> Moreover, in 2003 veteran Irian Jaya explorer Ralf Kiesel confirmed to me that since 1995 there have been persistent rumours of Thylacines existing in at least two sections of Irian Jaya's Baliem Valley - the Yali area in the valley's northeast region, and the NP Carstenz in its southwest. The latter area is of particular significance because back in the early 1970s Jan Sarakang, a Papuan friend of Kiesel, had a most startling experience while working with a colleague in the mountains just west of NP Carstenz.

> They had built a camp for some geologists near Puncac Jaya at an altitude of roughly 1.5 miles and were sitting by their tents that evening, eating their meal, when two unfamiliar dog-like animals emerged from the bush.

> One was an adult, the other a cub, and both appeared pale in colour, but most striking of all was their stiff, inflexible tails, and the incredible gape of their jaws when they yawned spasmodically. Clearly drawn by the smell of the food, the two animals walked nervously from side to side, eyeing the men and their food supplies, and approaching to within 20 yards. Eventually the cub became bold enough to walk up to the men, who tried to feed it, but when one of them also tried to catch it, the cub bit his hand and both animals then ran back into the bush and were not seen again.

The men should have been fully conversant with dingoes and, as Dr Shuker pointed out, the tail and the yawn are both indicative of the Thylacine. The only thing missing was the stripes, and that could be the result of the lighting.

So there the situation rests.

---

17   Shuker, Karl 2012. 'The New Guinea Thylacine – crying wolf in Irian Jaya?' http://karlshuker.blogspot.com.au/2013/05/the-new-guinea-Thylacine-crying-wolf-in.htm (last accessed 9 May 2013)

~~~

Malcolm Smith is a retired public servant who originally studied zoology at the University of Queensland and Macquarie University, Sydney. He is the author of Bunyips and Bigfoots: In Search of Australia's Mystery Animals (1996).

Apart from papers based on his M.Sc. studies on koalas, he has contributed to the now defunct journal, Cryptozoology, and the more recent, Journal of Cryptozoology, as well as a review of the Thylacine in the 1982 anthology on carnivorous marsupials. He operates a cryptozoology blog, http://malcolmscryptids.blogspot.com.au

The 'Ozenkadnook Tiger' or 'OK Tiger', a photograph of a rather mysterious-looking creature some speculate may be a Thylacine, was taken by Rilla Martin in 1964. Martin took the photo near Goroke in Western Victoria, and its authenticity has been the subject of constant debate since its publication by the *Wimmera Mail-Times*.

CHAPTER 6

Quest for the Thylacine

by Peter Chapple

Reports of mystery animals in Australia - according to some writers on the subject - commenced only two years after the settlement of New South Wales. As the human population spread in all directions, in the process irretrievably changing the landscape, nearly all districts developed their own local animal legend. These beasts were typically of the carnivorous type. The infant media industry was quick to seize upon these stories and many local legends became nationally famous as a result, including the 'Tantanoola Tiger' of South Australia (1884-1895), the 'Gippsland Tiger' of Victoria (1930s), the 'HelioThylacine' of Western Australia (1920s) and the 'Marsupial Tiger' of Queensland (1872-1970s).

The general descriptions of these creatures fitted three main forms. There were large cat-like animals, variously described as spotted, striped, or a uniform black, grey or brown. There were striped dog-like creatures, in all ways similar to, or even identical to, the Thylacine (*Thylacinus cynocephalus*), as described in 1803 from a Tasmanian type specimen, and lastly a water-dwelling creature of widely varying description, which received some historical support from the (possibly misinterpreted) early accounts of the Victorian Aboriginal legend of the 'bahn-yip' or 'bunyip'.

There are also reports of a bobcat or caracal-like animal, and what may prove to be a mainland form of the Tasmanian devil. For the purposes of this paper the author has chosen to ignore the reports of panther and puma-like cats, and concentrate upon the current research into mainland Tasmanian devils and mainland Thylacines.

THE AUSTRALIAN RARE FAUNA RESEARCH ASSOCIATION INC.

I began my personal investigations into the possible existence of Tasmanian devils and Thylacines on the Australian mainland in August 1981. Within a few years, I had gathered some 300 reported sightings and other related information. It became obvious, however, that I had no hope of succeeding on my own. I needed to form an organisation to collect, collate and research the incoming material.

In 1984, I founded what is now known as the Australian Rare Fauna Research Association Inc. (ARFRA) a band of enthusiasts that has worked tirelessly and without ever losing faith in our ultimate success for more than 17 years. We have confronted scepticism and ridicule from many directions.

However, we have been inspired by the support we have had from the thousands of eyewitnesses we have interviewed. They come from all walks of life, housewives, doctors, police, labourers, politicians, sports- persons, teachers and so on. The most supportive group has been, without doubt, the farmers and graziers, people who earn their living from the land, and are not likely to fabricate sightings or misidentify common wild animals. These are the people who have come to ARFRA, asking for our assistance. Few of them have any interest in seeing the animals destroyed: in fact, most seem determined to preserve their local wildlife, and thus, tend to steer clear of the government departments for fear of creating havoc.

ARFRA has collected and analysed some 4,300 sightings of Thylacines from the mainland of Australia, around 1,400 of which are highly credible. In addition, there is tantalising evidence to support the existence of the Tasmanian devil.

THE TASMANIAN DEVIL MIGRATES TO THE MAINLAND?

The Tasmanian devil (*Sarcophilus harrisi*), is today relatively quite common in Tasmania, although evidence strongly suggests that it suffered a decline during the early 20th century. As a scavenger, the devil is admirably suited to life as a camp follower of the Thylacine. However, without the Thylacine in the present Tasmanian food chain, how is it that the devil has now become so successful and widespread? The favoured theory conjectures that the Thylacine once preyed heavily on young devils, keeping their numbers in check. I believe that the devil has prospered as a scavenger through the ever-increasing decimation of Tasmanian wildlife by motor vehicles.

In quite recent times, members of the genus *Sarcophilus* - either the Tasmanian species or a similar mainland form, which has been speculatively named *lanigera* - were widespread and possibly quite common across much of mainland southern Australia. Their bones have been found in Aboriginal kitchen middens along the Murray River, indicating that they were extant up to about four hundred years ago. Intriguingly, in the past 100 years, devil specimens have been taken from several parts of Victoria, including near Melbourne (1903), Tooborac (1912) and the Enfield Forest near Ballarat (1971 and 1974). During 1987, while investigating a number of alleged sightings in the Harcourt area of central Victoria, members of ARFRA found and photographed footprints in a dry creek bed. Subsequently, similar tracks were plaster cast in a number of other centres very much further to the east.

Dr Eric Guiler, an authority on Tasmanian mammals, identified these as being Tasmanian devil tracks. We have also heard vocalisations of devils several times while doing fieldwork in Victoria. The *Maryborough & District Advertiser* (Vic) published an article soon after our footprint find, in which we claimed to have found evidence of devils in the Harcourt district, and also in the Healesville region, many kilometres to the east. We were overwhelmed with silence. Then on March 28, 1991, a female devil was struck and killed by a car at Harcourt, and three days later a juvenile male was badly injured when run over by a car at Yellingbo, about 1.5km west of Healesville, and subsequently died. The two carcasses have been kept in deep freeze but DNA work conducted to establish the genetic origin of these two animals has so far proven 'inconclusive', perhaps because the test was conducted to prove the specimens were of Tasmanian origin, a theory not able to be established. Further tests are apparently about to take place.

THE THYLACINE - GREATEST MYSTERY OF THEM ALL

Like the Tasmanian devil, the Thylacine, *Thylacinus cynocephalus*, was once widespread on continental Australia, of which Tasmania was at that time a great peninsula. However, the land bridge between Tasmania and the mainland was inundated some twelve thousand years ago. With the advent of the dingo, *Canis dingo*, presumably introduced some thousands of years ago to northern Australia, the mainland Thylacines - or so goes the current thinking - were placed under population pressure by this far more sophisticated and successful predator occupying the same ecological niche. Eventually, the Thylacine was exterminated from the mainland. Only on the island of Tasmania did it survive.

This is a very simplistic explanation as to why the Thylacine is no longer part of mainland Australian fauna. However, it fails to address the continued sightings across broad areas of the mainland ever since, including apparently documented sightings by eminent explorers during the early 1800s in Victoria and SA (I have yet to see these records - PC). By choosing to disregard the thousands of mainland sightings, Australian biologists were able to conclude that the Thylacine was extinct worldwide by 1986. This was exactly 50 years after the last captive Thylacine died in the Hobart Zoo. Let us look a little at the Thylacine as an extant species in Tasmania and then in more detail at its mainland history.

First described in 1803 from an animal captured near Hobart, the Thylacine, as is usual with predators, was never particularly common in Tasmania. Nonetheless, its depredations on the introduced flocks of sheep and other domestic livestock soon gave the animal a bad reputation.

During the 1830s, it was considered enough of a pest to have a bounty placed on its head by the Van Dieman's Land Company. Thousands were killed, yet even then, so determined were many of the early settlers that the animal be exterminated altogether that, in the 1880s, the Tasmanian Government provided the impetus for thousands more Thylacines to be destroyed when they also introduced a bounty scheme on the Tiger. Massive burning of the forests, both deliberately and accidentally, must have killed many more Thylacines, devils and quolls. Further pressure on Thylacine numbers resulted from trappers collecting for zoos.

Although apparently an uninteresting exhibit, at different times the animal was kept in zoos in Hobart, Melbourne, Sydney and Adelaide within Australia, and Berlin, Antwerp, London and New York Zoos overseas. By the mid-1920s, it was observed the animal was becoming more difficult to find, and its price as a zoo specimen climbed accordingly. As far as is known, no further specimens were captured for zoos after 1933.

One of the largest marsupial carnivores ever - a big male is at least as large as a big German Shepherd dog - the Thylacine is a formidable hunter, although evidently quite mild in disposition for the most part. The most noticeable distinguishing features are the series of stripes on the hindquarters, the long semi-rigid kangaroo-like tail, and the peculiar hind limb structure, also kangaroo-like. It has a dog-like head, but with the ears being set well back at the base of the skull, again like those of a kangaroo, and hooded over somewhat. The animal has an enormous gape of at least 85 degrees, and extremely strong jaw muscles, which often give the head the appearance of being proportionally too large for the body. The adult male is larger and taller than the female.

Many anecdotes exist about the behaviour of the Thylacine, but as much of it is based entirely on hearsay, and is not supported by all the accounts, I have chosen to leave the stories aside for the moment. Suffice it to say that ARFRA has found supportive evidence for only some of the yarns, but much of what we now believe to be factual about the animal's ecology has never been written in any publication. Interestingly, some of the documented anecdotal quotes which have been most ridiculed by the scientific fraternity appear to be the very same stories which receive the most support from modern-day accounts.

THE MAINLAND LEGEND STARTS

In 1884, a young man riding home from a dance became the first to officially see the legendary 'Tantanoola Tiger' of South Australia. It was described as 'large and grinning with satin stripes and carrying a whole sheep in its mouth'. The animal was seen quite frequently in the district over the next decade, and the descriptions given of it basically tallied with the Thylacine. Then in 1895, a man called Donovan shot an animal on a property outside the town and took the carcass to the Tantanoola Hotel. The stuffed remains may be seen there today. It is neither a genuine tiger nor a Thylacine, but most resembles a dog or dingo.

While driving in western Victoria in 1964, Miss Rilla Martin of Melbourne, was surprised to see an animal standing on the edge of light scrub some distance from the unmade road on which she was driving. She stopped the car, wound down the window, and took a 'happy snap' of the creature before it dashed off into the scrub and away. She told the relatives with whom she was staying of the incident, but they disbelieved her. Upon returning home to Melbourne, Miss Martin had the film developed and sent the photo to her relatives with the comment, 'Here is the photograph of the animal that I told you about and you laughed at me'. Her relatives took the photo to the local newspaper office, and Rilla Martin became an - albeit reluctant - media personality. After considerable analysis, and a number of quite serious aspersions being cast, the photograph was declared a hoax. While no one openly accused Miss Martin of any impropriety, she disappeared into anonymity, refusing any further debate on the matter. The animal became known as the 'Ozenkadnook Tiger', after the location where it was seen.

In 1966, the carcass of an adult Thylacine was discovered in a limestone cave under the Nullarbor Plain near Mundrabilla, Western Australia, and the second in as many years to be discovered under the Plain. The discoverers, both scientifically trained, were initially very excited, because the carcass looked to be very fresh. It still had sufficient hair to show the dorsal stripes, and was still being fed upon by scavengers. However, carbon dating suggested it was approximately 3,000 years old - some authorities say 4,500 years. This was a controversial conclusion, argued against on the grounds that when discovered, the carcass still had an intact eyeball and a strong odour of decay. The carcass is often referred to today as having been found in a mummified state, but as pointed out by Athol Douglas (1986) it was definitely not mummified. The Mundrabilla carcass remains the greatest enigma of all, in that, if it is around 3,000 years old, it becomes just another piece of fossil evidence in establishing the past distribution of the Thylacine on the mainland. If, however, as Douglas maintains, it was fresh when found, it is the strongest recent hard evidence gathered of the animal's continued existence, Also, as many experts have covertly told me, the carbon dating method is not considered strictly accurate for relatively fresh material, and can be affected by several outside factors.

Of the 4,400 alleged Thylacine sightings from the mainland in ARFRA's extensive database, over three thousand are from southeastern Australia. The spread of these sightings is enormous, covering at least 80 per cent of Victoria and much of southeastern NSW and southeastern South Australia. However, not all of the sightings are credible. While the majority of observers genuinely believe that they have seen something unusual, a goodly percentage of the sightings can be discounted as having been of unusual-looking dogs, kangaroos and mange-infested foxes. After stringent analysis, ARFRA has eliminated nearly 2,000 of the Victorian sightings from serious study, but this still leaves just over 1,200 which appear to be very good descriptions of Thylacines.

In 1984 the author became closely involved in Thylacine research on the mainland. A story was shown on Melbourne television concerning a photograph that had allegedly been taken of a Thylacine in south-central Victoria. Typically, the photo showed a mangy fox, but it did allow me to put out a public appeal for further information and reports. I was inundated, and ARFRA was formed.

We at ARFRA decided to tackle the subject on two fronts. Firstly, if Thylacines really do exist on the mainland, we reasoned that there ought to be some physical evidence in the form of footprints, kills and perhaps a skin or two. Secondly, thousands of hours of library research needed to be done to gather as much archival material as possible from old newspapers, diaries and the like. There were hundreds of sightings in government files, lying unstudied. ARFRA needed to collate this material to give us our historical database.

We quickly became aware of the primary difficulty of the serious Thylacine researcher. Very little fieldwork was conducted on the Thylacine in Tasmania during its heyday there, and much of the 'knowledge' of the animal has been gleaned from the reminiscences of early settlers and hunters. There are no existing tape recordings of Thylacine vocalisations, no photographs of conclusive Thylacine faeces or faecal analysis, and no known historical plaster casts of the spoor of living Thylacines.

The method by which today's biologists obtain Thylacine footprints is to use the feet of museum specimens pressed into damp sand. As we have found, the spoor of a living Thylacine bears little resemblance to these 'museum creations'. Various authors have depicted the spoor of a Thylacine, based upon information provided them by early hunters. Dr. Eric Guiler compared Thylacine spoor with that of other - common Tasmanian mammals. It is evident that under certain conditions, and as shown by some zoo photographs of the 1930s, the Thylacine sometimes crouched so as to leave an extended 'heel' behind the plantar pad. Interestingly, although the Thylacine spoor - both front and hind foot - is considerably different to that of a dog, some remarkable similarities can be evident on occasions.

While ARFRA has worked mainly in Victoria on footprint searches, interested people in other mainland states have found their own evidence. Sid Slee (1987), a farmer from south-western Australia, assisted by Aboriginal researcher Kevin Cameron, found tracks on his large grazing property, while Dawn Anderson and Kath Alcock (1970) took photos and plaster casts of tracks associated with a sighting of their own. Some of the Slee and Anderson footprints, as well as some found by ARFRA, show the extended 'heel' on the hind-foot impression. Mooney (1984) depicts the Thylacine's spoor as being trilobate, and casts taken by ARFRA in Victoria in 1990 and since have been very similar to Mooney's diagram.

As mentioned previously, the Thylacine has a massive bite, due to its enormous gape, strong sharp teeth and extremely powerful jaws. The bite has been likened to the shearing action of a pair of huge bolt-cutters, more than enough to remove the head of a largish prey animal from the body.

It is often stated that the Thylacine has a jaw gape of 120 degrees: I have seen two published accounts claiming 180 degrees! Work done by Moeller (1997) shows that no published photograph of a Thylacine 'yawning' has a gape of more than 80 degrees. Former zoo trapper of Thylacines, Mr Adye Milner Jordan wrote in 1987 of another aspect of the Thylacine's feeding methods, in which he described the animal biting off the two front legs of the victim, and placing its front feet in the holes thus created. Then, by pulling upwards on the trunk of the victim's body with its teeth, it literally pulls the body out of the skin. The skin is then left and the body taken away. ARFRA has observed kills showing this unique feeding pattern on a number of occasions.

The Thylacine as a predator, exhibits feeding patterns as a response to the different food preferences of individual animals, as well as the necessarily different modes for dealing with a variety of prey. Therefore, in addition to decapitation and peeling out of the body, ARFRA and others have noted other feeding methods, such as would appear to be alien to the behaviour of dingoes/dogs and other known predators. Researchers have found decapitated kangaroos which have been eaten down through the shoulder into the rib-cage with the heart and lungs removed, while Sid Slee and others have found carcasses where the only feeding damage is from blood feeding around the throat.

Another most individualistic feeding method noted in the Ozenkadnook region, as well as - occasionally - in ARFRA's main study zone, has been the biting of a hole behind the shoulder of a sheep whereupon the predator's head is protruded into the chest cavity and the heart and lungs removed that way. Dr. Eric Guiler (1998) records the finding of a sheep with the skull opened and the brain eaten, and suggests that this is a typical Thylacine predation method. Again, we have found similar kills in Victoria.

In 1998, I commenced a thesis at Monash University, Melbourne, using 1,080 good to excellent sightings logged by ARFRA in conjunction with the computer program BIOCLIM, first developed by Dr. Henry Nix and his colleagues at the CSIRO, Canberra. This work has since been translocated to the Australian National University in Canberra. In brief, BIOCLIM considers each sighting against thirty-five topographical and climatic variables, based upon observations, which have been collected on the known climate of each sighting location. While the program has some critics, a number of interesting patterns appear to be emerging from this study. Perhaps one of the more disturbing aspects which BIOCLIM appears to be outlining is that, while the number of alleged mainland Thylacine sightings has increased in every decade since the 1950s, the actual geographic dispersal of these sightings has shown a marked decline, particularly marked in the 1980s and 1990s charts. A number of possible reasons for this decline are being considered, but destruction of former Thylacine habitat appears to be the strongest theme.

As would be expected with a predatory animal about which so little is known, photographic evidence of a wild Thylacine is minimal, and in all truth, none of what we have seen is beyond conjecture. As should indeed be the case, when an animal is being filmed opportunistically without any previous expectation, nearly all such photographs we have been shown lapse into the grainy imperfections of the holiday snapshot. In 1957 a helicopter pilot took a photograph of an animal running along the beach at Birthday Bay, in southwestern Tasmania. The photo was inconclusive. Part-Aboriginal naturalist and tracker Kevin Cameron, took at least two photographs of an animal he claimed to be a Thylacine in WA in November, 1984, but doubts have been expressed by some as to their authenticity. Even Athol Douglas, Cameron's staunchest supporter, has stated that he 'had doubts about the health of the animal', even though he still believes it to have been a Thylacine.

In 1971, a young Victorian couple on holiday in SA took a 8mm movie film of an animal they were sure was a Thylacine as it ran across in front of their car. The film was taken under difficult conditions, and the wife was unfamiliar with the camera she was forced to use, but the images are extremely interesting.

Most of the other photographs we have seen, only some of which we have in our archives, have been definitely of foxes or dogs. Two inconclusive photos taken by the author in 1987 will be published in a forthcoming book on the subject. Most recently, Czech researcher Ivan Mackerle took video footage in June 2000, of what he believes was a Thylacine-like animal in North Queensland, but as I have yet to see it, I cannot comment at this stage.

In concluding this brief account, it should be made clear that there is much more which could be said on the subject. ARFRA's ambition is to be able to apply its knowledge of the animal towards the gaining of conclusive photographic evidence - evidence that would need to be handled with the utmost security. Hopefully after that stage is reached, we would like to continue our involvement in ongoing research into the Thylacine, and the formulation of a practical conservation strategy for the species, including captive breeding programs.

We at ARFRA have learned the hard way that it is impossible to get government backing to search for or conduct research on an animal once it has officially been declared extinct. The official attitude is: 'The Thylacine is extinct. Therefore, why look for it?' I ask, on whose authority was this highly significant decision taken, and based upon which particular twenty-year study? I can only say that it has taken me 20 years of dedicated research to be satisfied in the belief that I know otherwise.

~~~

Peter Chapple was founder and Life Governor of the Australian Rare Fauna Research Association Inc (ARFRA). Before his death in 2001, Peter was working towards his Masters of Science at Monash University, analysing patterns of distribution of recent Thylacine sightings. This overview of contemporary Thylacine research was originally presented by Peter Chapple at the 2001 Myths & Monsters Conference and is reproduced here with the kind permission of ARFRA and his wife, Rosemary Chapple.

Ray Harvey's game camera took this photo of a faintly striped animal at 8.05am on 22 May 2012 in south-east Queensland. Could it be a Thylacine variant? *Courtesy of Ray Harvey.*

CHAPTER 7

Evidence for the continuing survival of the Thylacine

by Gary Opit

T he Thylacine (*Thylacinus cynocephalus*) was the largest living marsupial carnivore at the time of European settlement of Australia and is generally believed that it existed only in Tasmania where it was hunted to extinction because it was a sheep killer, the last captive Thylacine dying on 7 September 1936. There has long been a general belief that the Thylacine must be extinct because of a lack of recent domestic animal killings attributable to it. However, recent scientific studies of Thylacine jaws have proven that the animals did not hunt sheep and kangaroos, as had been believed, simply because it was a dog-sized predator. Its jaws were so weak that it would have been restricted to hunting much smaller prey, according to researchers from the University of New South Wales. In spite of the Thylacine's 30kg body mass and carnivorous diet, its weak jaws limited it to small, agile prey, such as possums and bandicoots (Boness 2011).

Robert Paddle, author of *The Last Tasmanian Tiger,* studied the detailed records of the Tasmanian Government and the various sheep farming companies and found that the species rarely ever preyed on domestic stock and was only occasionally observed, killed or captured (Paddle 2000). Eric Guiler, author of several articles and books on Thylacines. Including *Tasmanian Tiger: A Lesson to be Learned,* also states that 'The tables of stock increases from Woolnorth from 1830-34 give no losses due to Thylacines nor do they pass comment on this topic although they record all sorts of other calamities' (Guiler, 1985, p.95).

The latest quantitative skeletal analysis undertaken by Borja Figueiredo and Christine Janis of Brown University on Rhode Island, USA, showed that unlike wolves and dogs that have their forepaws 'locked in' for running, Thylacines have highly flexible, manipulative forearms, with an elbow allowing for both pronation and supination of the forearm.

This would indicate that it is not a pursuit predator, the animal would be more catlike and that it may also have the ability to climb trees (Figueiredo and Janis 2011).

The Thylacine is believed to have gone extinct on mainland Australia around 3000 years ago and this is generally believed to have occurred due to competition from the introduction of the dingo around that time. However, Paddle does not agree with this assumption and states 'There is little evidence that the European introduction of dogs into Tasmania was a direct factor in the Thylacine's extinction' (Paddle 2000). Consequently, he believes that competition with dogs is unlikely to have exterminated the Thylacine across an entire continent.

Paddle conclusively shows that it was an epidemic disease that devastated Thylacine numbers both in the wild and in captivity. In his article 'The Thylacine's last straw: epidemic disease in a recent mammalian extinction' in the journal *Australian Zoologist* he states:

> The disease was episodic, recurring every two to four months (until full recovery or death), with no evidence of seasonal variation. Its initial appearance, at present, appears to have occurred in northeastern Tasmania, around St Helens, in1896... The over-all effect of the disease in the wild, post 1896 was an increased rate of dead specimens presented for public and private bounties... The initial expression of the disease in Thylacines, from 1896 to 1910, saw massive, clumped, significant hair loss, with exposed skin consisting of deep-seated, actively bleeding lesions... The mid-period expression of the disease, from 1911 to 1925, saw it largely expressed as minor, spotted hair loss, with bleeding active on the exposed skin, accompanied by reduced levels of mortality. The late-period expression of the disease, from 1926 to 1936, saw at a minimum, poor coat and condition, with widespread, but not clumped, loss of hair, and no overt sign of bleeding, to at a maximum, a return of the significant, large scale hair loss and bleeding typical of the initial expression. (Paddle 2012).

No living specimens were ever obtained on mainland Australia, where it is known from fossil bones retrieved from localities across the continent, or from New Guinea. However, a near-perfect carcass was recovered in 1966 by Western Australian Museum scientists from a cave, now known as Thylacine Hole, on Mundrabilla station and it is now on exhibition in the Western Australian Museum.

This was not a dehydrated carcass; the skin and hair was largely intact with the characteristic dark bars clearly visible, the tongue and left eyeball recognisable and a musty odour of decomposition noticeable. It looked like a recently dried-out carcass after the maggots had left but before the hide and fur-eating invertebrates had begun to feed.

Dry tissues from under the carcass were carbon[14] dated at the University of Sydney and an age of 4,500 years was obtained. However, Athol Douglas, a scientific staff member for 40 years at the Western Australian Museum and who eventually became the Senior Experimental Officer, believed that the carbon[14] date is inaccurate because of contamination by the ground water, which had saturated the carcass. He stated:

> During my 1986 visit to the cave, I found a dingo carcass; it was hairless, dry and odorless, and its skin was like parchment. The Thylacine carcass had been – and is – in a far superior state of preservation than this dingo carcass, yet the dingo carcass could not have been in the cave for more than twenty years, as the Western Australian Museum party had removed all specimens and bones in 1966… The (Thylacine) carcass may have been only months old at the time it was found. This carcass represents strong evidence of the existence of the Thylacine in very recent times. It is also significant that recent sighting reports have come from Mundrabilla Station and the surrounding area. (Douglas 1990)

In the Sydney Morning Herald 02/03/2005, under the headline 'Genuine Thylacine spotters earn their stripes,' the writers Deborah Smith and Richard Macey state 'Robert Paddle, author of *The Last Tasmanian Tiger,* said up to 4000 sightings of the stripey animals have been made on the mainland or in Tasmania since they were declared extinct in 1937… it was important not to dismiss all sightings as rubbish…I have spoken to about five or six people (who believe they have seen a Tasmanian tiger) and have been impressed by their knowledge of the local environment and the flora and fauna.' (Smith and Macey 2005).

The Thylacine was known to have a very powerful sense of smell and it has been reported that captive individuals on farms in Tasmania in the 1800s became restless 20 minutes before the humans could detect the approach of visitors.

Tom Billett, a farmer and fur trapper from northwestern Tasmania, informed Col Bailey that he saw Thylacines when he was young and how extremely shy and cunning they were. He last saw a Thylacine when he snared one in the early 1950s, which escaped when he was trying to force it into a chaff bag. 'By crikey they were cunning devils. They could smell a man from miles away, and my best two hunting dogs would run like hell when there was a tiger about, they were too cunning an animal to show themselves willingly.' (Bailey 2001) Thylacines lived successfully with humans for something like 50,000 years and it is to be expected that they developed the ability to avoid humans. Scientific investigations indicate that it preys on common small mammals, can detect dogs and humans at great distances, actively avoids them and rarely vocalizes. Physical remains are an essential part of zoology and our understanding of our biodiversity is based on specimens stored in research establishments such as museums. However, reported observations make up a vast quantity of data for many species and physical evidence may only become available infrequently.

Professor Michael Archer is so positive that the species is extinct that he compared the pattern of Thylacine sightings to flying saucer sightings, based on a comparison made by Ralph Molnar of the Queensland Museum in 1984. Both, he writes, are primarily concerned with observations of unexplainable phenomena over brief periods of time associated with poor visibility and few observers (Archer 1997, Molnar 1984). Molnar and Archer appear to be saying that, when humans are alone and observe something unusual with poor visibility during a brief period of time, it invariably resolves itself into either a flying saucer or a Thylacine.

Archer describes how originally he open-mindedly followed up reports of Thylacines on the mainland while working for the Western Australian and Queensland museums until he observed a small black and white pig cross the road in front of him and thought at first that it looked very much like a Tasmanian devil. From this experience he developed the idea that people who saw Tasmanian tigers were also suffering from a similar delusion that he himself suffered upon seeing a small pig. However, almost anyone else, beyond a zoologist, would not have an image of a Tasmanian devil in their mind as they drove around on the mainland. Anyone else observing the same small black and white animal would have most likely thought that they must have been viewing a dog or a cat or a small pig or goat.

Until the recent publicity of the dreadful mouth cancer disease affecting the devil's survival, most people regarded the Tasmanian devil as an animated character in Bugs Bunny cartoons.

Almost everyone that I have ever spoken to on the mainland were unclear as to exactly what a Tasmanian devil and a Tasmanian tiger actually looked like and which one was which, if they were not the same animal. Unlike zoologists, the majority of the population has almost no interest in either animal or anything else not closely related to their wellbeing. Almost everybody that reported Thylacine-like sightings to me over many years had little or no knowledge of Thylacines.

Many scientists and other writers dismiss Thylacine sighting reports. Roger Martin, while studying mammals in north Queensland stated 'I struck up a conversation with an old man who had spent many years in the area...when he interrupted and asked whether I'd seen any tigers. The big fellas! I politely steered the conversation off in another direction...I concluded that the old man was hallucinating when he saw his tigers.' (Martin 1999).

There are two methods of interpreting reported observations. The first method is to deny these sightings and claim that all these observations come from hallucinations because there is no back-up physical evidence. Apparently, these hallucinations only occur if a striped animal is observed. It implies that thousands of everyday people from all walks of life regularly have such profound hallucinations, often while driving, that they are compelled to inform the authorities. Yet this conclusion finds no parallels in the safety of the thousands of drivers and there are almost no accidents due to hallucinations.

By looking at the patterns in the data we can attempt to establish a consensus of what is real and what is not. People have a vast array of cultural entities stored within their minds that have come from a variety of sources, be they books, films or traditions. Everything from goblins and ogres to hobbits, unicorns and fairies inhabit the forests of the mind with dragons and witches on broomsticks flying through the air. But no human ever seems to observe and report on any of these manifestations and no hallucinations appear to include such entities.

Of the two methods of interpreting these reported observations, the second method is to accept these reported observations and to examine them to see if there are correlations with known facts about the Thylacine. Ongoing sighting reports provide evidence that the Thylacine has survived as viable populations in many parts of its original range in diverse habitats from arid lands to rainforest, particularly on the mainland where it has been reputedly encountered repeatedly in temperate, subtropical and tropical climatic zones. This is to be expected from a family that evolved in Australia and this last species of Thylacinidae has had a long history as a predator across the continent.

The reports that I have collected suggest the survival of a small number of these animals originally in the rugged wilderness of mountain ranges such as the Grampians, Great Divide, Nightcap, Macpherson and the Border Ranges. With the removal of Aboriginal hunters, dingoes and wild dogs, a relict Thylacine population has increased and now they are being observed in the coastal nature reserves. Some researchers have spent years searching localities where it has been reported and have set up automatic cameras that photograph anything that moves past. That is how Ray Harvey was able to take the tantalising photo at the beginning of this article at 8.05 am on the 22 May 2012 in south-east Queensland. Could this be the first photograph of an endangered species that is supposed to be extinct?

Ongoing sighting reports, if we believe them, provide evidence that the Thylacine, particularly on the mainland, has a range of fur colours and degree of fur length, as perhaps would be expected for a species that is liable to have had isolated populations in different habitats and climate zones over millions of years. The reports contain information that both short-furred and long-furred populations occur. The range of fur colours includes the most common sightings of animals with short light brown fur with dark brown stripes across the back. However, Thylacines have been observed on many occasions to have light brown stripes that merge with the background fur so that no stripes are visible or only discernible at close range. Conversely, the species has been observed to have a dark colour phase in which the entire animal is covered in very dark brown fur.

The long-furred animals are covered in thicker fur and always have a thickly furred tail, usually with distinct rings visible. As in the short-furred Thylacines, the fur colour can have the same range with the body covered in a light brown fur with dark stripes, light brown stripes that blend with the background fur colour and dark brown fur. We are indebted to Carl Lentz for the most detailed description and Aboriginal name 'Punchum' of this mystery mammal. He shot one of these animals on Tallai hill behind Mudgerabah, in the Gold Coast hinterland in 1894 in southeast Queensland. Carl Lentz writes:

> It was as big as an Alsatian (German shepherd) dog. We tied its legs together with tough vines and stuck a long pole through them, by which we carried it home about half a mile (.8 km). It was heavy. I intended to take it to Nerang 10 miles (16 km) away by pack horse the next day and send it by train to the Brisbane Museum but owing to heavy rains all night causing the creek to flood we couldn't make the journey to Nerang so we measured it and skinned it instead.

> From the tip of the nose to the end of its long thick black tail it measured 6 feet (1828 mm), height of shoulder 25 inches (635 mm), around the chest 23 inches (584 mm). It was long in the body and strongly built on the forequarters, but more slightly built around the waist and hindquarters. It had 2 extra long sharp fang teeth, one and five eighth inches long (35 mm) besides the 4 ordinary incisor teeth. It was a magnificent, male, specimen.

The forehead and face was a light bronze colour. It had 5 bright orange rings of very short hair around its eyes, which were purplish-brown in colour. It had a short thick coat of light pale blue-grey and white stripes running downwards with bright, marble-sized orange to yellow spots along the flanks. Above this short thick coat from the back of the head covering the body it has a dark thin coat of black hairs and this makes it appear to be a brindled colour when seen from a distance. Its tail also has the same white and blue-grey rings, each 20 mm wide, beneath the same outer covering of long black hair.

After this, I heard of a similar experience, which happened to Gilston's first pioneer, Mr. William Duncan who related his story to me of how he shot one in 1850. There are a few at large yet in remote places and they are the greatest of sneaks and night prowlers. I have seen one of the beasts since on a wallaby track at night near a road. I was able to make him out very clearly when he passed through the beam of light from the car's headlight that made his eyes glow. But when we searched for him, together with some friends, a little while later, all we could find were his tracks, the size of very big dog tracks. (Lentz 1967, 1984 and Hall *et al* 1988).

In the spring of 1969 I was fortunate enough to observe the animal. My sighting tallied almost exactly with the animal shot by Lentz. The location was the Brisbane - Gold Coast Highway, between Brisbane and Beenleigh, a single lane each way through rural cattle grazing land and moist open forest instead of the urban sprawl that has since replaced it. At about 11 pm, as I travelled south through long stretches of darkened forest with very little other traffic, a large carnivorous marsupial crossed the road directly in front of my vehicle.

I saw its head protrude from the vegetation in front of the car and watched it walk onto the bitumen and cross the road in an unhurried manner. It stood approximately 60-cm at the shoulders, had a body length of about 75-cm and a tail of the same length. The snout protruded from a large head with a powerfully built body covered in brindled thick fur. The fore and hind legs were the same size and what was distinctly noticeable was a marsupial-like waddling gait that particularly caught my attention. It reminded me of the gait of a brush-tailed possum only this animal was very much larger. It had a long straight thickly furred tail with seven bands across it and this very distinctive banded tail was the last I saw of the animal as it disappeared into thick vegetation on the western side of the road. The tail in my drawing of the animal below is probably much thicker than it actually was. The tail did not make much of an impression on me when I was watching it cross the road as I scanned the movements of all of its body parts. However, it appeared very large as I concentrated on the banded tail when that was the only portion of the body that I could see as it entered the forest.

I am as interested in the Thylacine as I am interested in all of our animals and plants. For decades I have undertaken fauna and flora surveys, taught students on the natural sciences and for 16 years have had a live-to-air wildlife segment on ABC North Coast NSW Local Radio. For the last decade these have been weekly broadcasts and I have to immediately identify all fauna species from listener's enquiries.

I have received sightings of almost every known animal, vertebrate and invertebrate that people have encountered. I keep a record of all enquiries and reports by the public of what they have seen. On very rare occasions I have received calls and emails describing Thylacine-like animals in northeastern NSW and have now collected 65 sightings of these.

The first, I was very much surprised to receive, was on Tuesday 18 November 1997 and then other listeners began to phone the radio station to report their own sighting of a Thylacine-like animal. All of these people, usually rural dwellers and workers, were familiar with their local wildlife and particularly of their domestic animals. When they saw an animal that they could not identify it was because it did not resemble a dog, a cat or a fox.

Their explanation for the existence of the strange animal before their eyes was not that it must have been a Tasmanian tiger or devil, animals that they were generally ignorant about because they do not live in Tasmania. They believed that it was simply a native animal that they were unfamiliar with, or an animal that someone had artificially created by breeding a dog with a kangaroo or wallaby. However, some people were aware of the Tasmanian tiger and were very surprised to observe an animal that resembled it, as everyone believed that it lived only in the island state and is very rare or extinct. I treat all of their enquiries about all of their sightings equally no matter what listeners claim to have encountered. There has never been any difference in their descriptions or emotions whether they relate information describing easily identifiable fauna or difficult to identify fauna. People just want to know what they have seen. The following are some of the most interesting accounts that I received. In 1970 schoolteacher Mark was working on a banana farm at Crabbes Creek in north-eastern NSW during the school holidays and as they descended from a forested ridge top at the end of the day, the owner's German Sheppard dog began growling at something sheltering within an old, partly collapsed banana-packing shed overgrown with vines. The dog rushed in to attack the animal and Mark, the farm owner and several other workers were surprised to see the dog backing out of the shed with an animal almost as large covered with brown stripes across its back and a thick, stiff, kangaroo-like tail. The strange animal had huge jaws that opened to an extent, greater than the dog, and it gave forth with a bizarre coughing bark-like sound unlike anything that they had heard before.

The farm owner yelled out 'It's a monster, we will have to kill it' and picking up a stone, threw it at the strange animal. The stone missed its mark and the animal, looking up, saw the people and ran at great speed up the slope with a very unusual gait. The dog and the people chased the animal into a large hollow log where it crouched to stare at them. The owner remarked that they would have to kill the animal, as he would not allow a monster to live on the farm. Then they all descended back through the bananas to head for home. The next day the farm owner brought up his rifle but the animal was gone and they never saw it again.

In 1988 at Cawongla near Kyogle on the roadside at night, Len saw a Thylacine-like animal showing distinct dark brown banding on the rump, hips, and legs and along the tail. The tail was thickly furred, which reminded him of a photo of a numbat. The bands were about 2cm wide and 6cm apart. The front paw was lifted up near the snout. The snout and the tail were held straight and the round ears were cocked up.

In 1989 on Terania Creek Road at The Channon, Peter saw a Thylacine-like animal showing distinct dark brown banding across the body running across the road at night in front of his car. The tail was thickly furred. Following this animal were three smaller identical animals. This is one of only two report of a mother and it's young that I have received.

In 2003 at Upper Main Arm, bush regenerator Mark had a close observation of a Thylacine-like animal at midday and observed its striped back and stiff tail as it stood near the roadside. Being an expert on wildlife identification he was positive that it was a Thylacine. It gave a strange coughing bark-like call and bounded away.

On 15 January 2003 at 9.30am, mailman Peter drove right up to a strange looking animal standing on an earth bank on the southern section of Stock Route Road, just behind Billinudgel. As tall as a medium-sized dog, it looked something like a whippet crossed with a kangaroo. It was covered with a fine short brown fur except for the rump and tail, which was bare skinned with individual hairs scattered evenly across it. It was completely unconcerned by the presence of his car and he closely examined it for 5 minutes before it walked off. Peter had been involved in greyhound racing for many years and so was positive that the animal was neither a dog nor a fox and appeared to be a carnivorous marsupial. This report is important because it is one of only two that I have received that describes the animal suffering from the disease described by Paddle 2012 and this individual had significant hair loss.

I received a photograph of an unusual animal in an email in 2006 from Adam who was working on the new freeway crossing Stock Route Road at Billinudgel: 'I'm working on the Brunswick Heads Bypass. One of the engineers here has seen this animal a few times and has managed to get a photo of it. He's actually seen it climbing a tree. You can't see in the photo but he says it's got stripes across its rump. Regards, Adam.'

On Monday 16 January 2006 at 3.30 am near Mullumbimby, Michael Stubbs, highly skilled in the identification of fauna and flora and Fabiola Oliver observed a strange animal coming towards them along the eastern side of the road. Michael drew the animal after their sighting and it is featured above.

Michael was able to examine the animal closely from only 2 metres away and observed that it was 60 to 70 cm high and 1.3m long, the length of the body quite long when compared to its height. It had a very long thin tail that drooped down then lifted up towards the end. It had a large head with golden eyes and widely separated rounded ears. It was covered with short golden-fawn fur with black shadowy marks on the fur tips across the rump like vague bands. Michael noticed that it had a distinct waddle of the back legs as it walked and he watched it turn away from him and saw that it had a white band at the end of the tail with a black tip. It then ran off under a barbed-wire fence to disappear into the regrowth vegetation.

On 15 February 2006 at Hastings Point, Rose described a strange dog-like animal that she saw while driving to work in the morning. It was grey with dark grey mottling on its rump like bands, it had distinctive large round ears and was quite unlike a dog or fox. In December 2006 at 9.30am she again saw the same animal with three young cubs chasing and playing together on the road. Then on 3 February 2007 on Jones Road at Yelgun; just after dark, I watched, for about five minutes, a Thylacine-like animal that measured approximately 1.75m in length and about .75m in height crouched in the middle of the road, adjacent the Billinudgel Nature Reserve. From head to tail it was very dark brown in colour, its rump was distinctly hunched, fore and hind legs were of the same size, and it was stationary with its head down sniffing the road.

It was illuminated by the headlights of my car approximately 20m in front of me and was unconcerned by the presence of my vehicle. After five minutes I drove slowly towards it and at about 10m in front of my car it suddenly raised its head and body, pushed with its hind legs and ran off the road into the vegetation on all four legs.

I observed this same dark individual a second time on 30 December 2007, when it bounded across the track right in front of me at dusk about a km east of where I saw it on 3 February 2007. I found the same animal resting in vegetation in the mid afternoon on 4 August 2009. I saw its dark brown head and shoulders as it rose from a resting position about 7 metres from me and it ran off to the south. Unlike a wallaby it did not thump its feet or make any noise as it moved off. Jesse was jogging along the track behind the beach when he observed this animal again in the Billinudgel Nature Reserve at 7 pm on 3 December 2012; he saw a long stiff, furry dark brown tail held horizontally ¾ across the path and about half a metre above the ground. Thinking at first that it was a fallen branch he realised as he reached the object that it was the tail of a large animal occupied, as if eating something. He was almost on top of it when the animal saw him, leapt, spun around and ran back across the track into the bush in front of him leaving large footprints 12cm long and 8cm wide with what looked like three pads in the sandy soil.

Kim Falconer wrote to me and reported an encounter that she had on 30 December 2008 at 6:15am adjacent bushland of Arakwal National Park near Broken Head Road, Byron Bay:

> I heard a loud sound like a cross between a guttural possum noise and a large dog retching. I ran outside to find my cat facing off with a dog-like creature 4 times its size. I've been a vet nurse for 20 years. It was not a dog. I was two to three metres from it for several minutes.

> It weighed about 18 kg, had fawn-coloured short dense fur and smelled of musk, like a mild possum odour. The animal's face was like a dingo/dog/wolf but with rounder ears. The body language of this animal was not canine and the eyes were very keen, watching in a way domestic dogs do not. It walked, trotted and loped. It was not afraid of me but backed away whenever I approached closer than 2-3 metres. She had a springy rocking-horse gait, moving quickly then holding very still, lifting her head. She didn't take her eyes off of me. She seemed extremely curious, cautious, but with no familiar dog body language. The coat was like a newly sheared sheep in look, short, uniform length, fawn to light brown, and very dense, not laying flat like a dog, cat or horse coat. No stripes but a hint of black on legs and ears, white muzzle, like you might see on an elderly dog, black nose. She was in good condition, no ribs showing. The impression was healthy and lean. Her

neck was long and the entire body was lithe, it was long in the flank. The tail was the least dog-like feature, very stiff like a broom handle, thick at the base, with short fur, and it didn't act like a dog's tail. It didn't taper, or wag. It was the vocalisation that really threw me. It was not a dog sound she made, nothing like it. More like a retching possum and it was surprisingly loud. The hocks were pronounced and low, it rocked back on them when it loped away. There's no doubt in my mind it was a Thylacine.

Zoologist Mary Gardner, driving to the Cape Byron lighthouse on 18 September 2011, saw a similar animal at 8pm and told me 'It was neither dog, nor dingo and certainly not a fox. It had full ears, a hard erect, rather round body, high in the shoulders, tall lean thin legs, looked like it could jump, long thin hard-looking tail and the faintest glimpse of darker stripes around the body.'

The first time I received a report of a mainland Thylacine was in January 1982 in the Grampian Mountain Range in western Victoria. I met Laurie and Judy Arnott, originally from Geelong, who used to take camping holidays in the Grampians with their sons before retiring and then moving to live in Victoria Valley. On learning that I was studying the animals they described to me an animal that they had once observed. They had been coming to Rocklands Reservoir for five years on Labour Day long-weekend camping trips and on Friday 5 March 1965 on Halloms Road, Skeleton Creek, in the Mooralla District in the early evening they slowed to open a gate. It was then that a strange animal leapt into the middle of the track five metres in front of their car. It showed no concern or fear of their now stationary vehicle.

The animal sat in a crouched position with its forelegs held up off the ground, its butt resting and its long thick tail held stiff and horizontally about 15 cm off the ground. It turned its head towards them and stared as if confused by the bright headlights. The head was held about a metre above the ground, the mouth was closed, and the nose and the eyes were dark. The eyes appeared wider apart than a dog, slanted and towards the sides of the face. The shoulders were muscular and the haunches even more powerful and merged into the tail which was about 18cm at its base. The tail was as long as the body, about 6cm wide, did not taper and ended abruptly without any tuft.

It was covered in short, sleek grey-brown fur, darker above, a lighter brown beneath and across the back was a series of dark brown stripes that merged into the background fur colour along their edges. The stripes were all the same width, but of different lengths, and continued more than halfway down the sides of the body where they narrowed to points. The stripes began behind the shoulders, where they were only short, and grew longer as they continued to the haunches. The first quarter of the tail was also striped.

It was about the size of a large red-necked wallaby and they thought that it was a wallaby of a species not known to them. It turned its head forward and dropped its forefeet to the ground and now they saw that both forelegs and hind legs were the same length, unlike a wallaby and they expected it now to walk off. To their further amazement it suddenly leapt as if a coiled spring was powering the hind legs. In one bound it sprung up and out of the headlight beam coming down on its forefeet and it vanished into the darkness in the direction it was originally proceeding in.

Although they continued to visit the area for many years they never saw the animal again, nor did they ever find out what it was. However, they met a honey farmer, Hubert Howell, who had a shed and his hives along the same track and on hearing their description of the strange animal, confided to them that he had been seeing the animals regularly for twenty years, at least once a fortnight. Because no one else would believe him that such a strange animal could exist, he no longer mentioned it. They became friends with the old honey farmer who taught them his craft and when they retired Hubert Howell gave them a block of land so that they could live nearby.

Hubert continued to see the animals regularly and would mention to Laurie and Judy 'I saw our mate again today' and would describe variations in the shades of colour of different individuals, until he moved his hives out of the area in 1971, as he grew too old to farm his honey. After Hubert died they never mentioned the animals to anyone else, because they had never met anyone interested in wildlife, until they met me. I told them that no animal of such a description was known to occur in Australia. I did not tell them that their description of the animal closely matched an extinct species known only from Tasmania.

I asked Laurie to draw a picture of the animal and he did so. They had offered me a caravan to spend the night on their property, or even to use as a base while undertaking my studies and I accepted their kind offer. I subsequently questioned them independently over the next few days on a number of subjects including the description of their strange animal and they believed that it must live only in their area and that except for Hubert; no one else had ever seen one. They thought this because if they ever mentioned it no one would believe them.

I finally showed them drawings of a Thylacine by Ella Fry in W. D. L. Ride's 1970 book *A Guide to the Native Mammals of Australia,* based upon photographs of captive animals. In the background is a Thylacine standing normally, in the foreground is a drawing of the Thylacine rearing up as the keeper rattled the bars of its pen. They were amazed to find that the animal was actually known and even illustrated in a book. They stated that the drawing of the Thylacine rearing up was very similar to the position of the animal that they observed, except that it was more crouched with its butt on the ground.

Consequently, Laurie and I visited the locality where the animals had been observed and searched other areas including an abandoned property named Bullawin Park where we found clear prints of a Thylacine's forefeet and hind foot. I camped for days beside a remote waterhole and although I obtained clear views of many different animals I never saw a Thylacine. We also questioned other farmers and eventually gathered other sighting reports. Lou Harris saw one on his sheep property in 1967 and his dogs caught up to it running on either side, but then came running scared back to their master with their tails between their legs. Peter McIntyre saw one cross the road at Moutajup between Hamilton and Dunkeld in 1971. Horace Beveridge had observed one at Victoria point in 1974. Finally Hubert Howell's wife and daughter saw one near the Victoria Valley golf course in 1978.

Eventually I continued further west into South Australia, travelling from one national park to another and it was in the Bangham, Frances and Western Flat localities that I again began to pick up Thylacine reports from local people while exploring the Bangham Conservation Park. Mrs Claire James told me that she had seen Thylacines on two occasions near her farm in 1970. The first was lying in the shade of a shrub one hot summer morning as she drove down her track and it got to its feet and walked off when it saw her driving slowly up to it. Her close view of its unusual head, the way its back sloped down to its long, thin straight tail and stripes much the same colour as the background fur proved it was something rare and unusual. Her second view of it was similar. During 1972 to 1973 she heard its very distinctive call near her farmhouse twice, 3 to 4 months apart, during full moon nights. Each time the far-carrying vocalization, consisting of a series of double calls, each separated by several seconds of silence, came from a group of pines 300 metres away and each time the calls continued for about half an hour. It made a grunting cough 'Heeerr', somewhat similar, but louder, to the sound that a kangaroo makes if alarmed, followed by a coughing bark 'Cahh', creating 'Heeerr- Cahh….Heeerr- Cahh…. Heeerr- Cahh…. Heeerr- Cahh' calls.

Lindsey Laurence, a farmer on My Mia Mia Road at Western Flat had a very close encounter with the Thylacine on a hot summer night in 1972 when he walked out the back door to turn off his water sprinkler and encountered it unexpectedly. It tried to run off but trapped itself in the corner of the yard that was fenced and as Lindsey approached to within 10 metres; it rose up onto its hind legs, opened its jaws remarkably wide and hissed loudly at him. Lindsey retreated and the Thylacine dropped back down onto its four feet and cantered off around the fence.

In Bordertown I spoke with Mrs Heather Parker, local ABC Radio reporter, who, with her husband, owned a sheep farm. Because of her job she had picked up quite a number of Thylacine sightings and told me that several famers' wives had been recording sightings and that Mrs J. Cobrico of Wonthaggi had collected 70 sightings since 1955. Heather gave me sightings reports from 3 September 1965 to 27 December 1978 when all reports ceased after large-scale land clearing commenced. The Thylacines were obviously breeding because at 9.45pm on Friday 1 November 1974 Barbara Adams of Frances was driving between Gap and Conkar Roads with her four children, the oldest being 14, when in the brilliant moonlight they all saw two young Thylacines in scuffling play on the road. The animals did not notice the car until it had driven up beside them and the family said that they were so close that they could have learnt out the windows and touched them. This sighting was published in the Naracoorte Herald 7 November 1974 and Barbara and the children described the animals as standing 12 inches tall, covered in sandy fur with dark stripes on their flanks, heads that reminded them a little of lion cubs, small ears, heavy hind quarters and smooth thin tails that sloped down towards the ground. Upon seeing the car beside them they both scuttled off under a fence and disappeared into the vegetation.

I have personally received approximately 90 detailed sightings of animals from South Australia, Victoria, western NSW, north-eastern NSW, south eastern Queensland and Cape York that closely match Thylacines in every way. All of these reports were received unexpectedly while talking to people about local wildlife. Unlike zoologist Roger Martin, I do not steer the conversation off in another direction if someone describes having observed an unusual animal and I certainly do not conclude that people must be hallucinating. I do not treat people arrogantly because they have seen something unusual.

We humans are an arrogant species, readily denying the possibility of anything that does not fit into our world-view. Scientists laugh at farmers who describe seeing an unusual animal and then become enraged when farmers refuse to believe in some scientific discovery such as global warming and climate change. Some Thylacine researchers believe the species survived for decades in Tasmania after 1936 without leaving any physical evidence because of detailed sighting reports. If their own searches fail to find evidence then they too can become convinced that the animal must be extinct because it eluded them.

In an uncertain world, people crave certainty. It is this that has elevated the Thylacine from an obscure animal in a remote location into a species that can make headlines around the world. How can an animal that is definitely extinct continue to be seen by large numbers of people?

The answer to this question is simply a refusal by zoologists to look at the evidence. Instead of stating that there is a continuous flow of reported sightings and that we will just have to wait and see whether the species is still around, they resort to the common human tendency of jumping to conclusions and 'shooting the messenger'. The thought of animals outwitting humans and of humans not knowing absolutely everything is anathema to them.

If they had studied physics and quantum mechanics such researchers may have understood that one cannot be positive about many things. The Thylacine appears to be able to avoid detection because of their ability to detect humans in advance and have probably been avoiding us for the 50,000 years that we have lived with them on this continent. Robert Paddle's research provides evidence that they were only ever collected in large numbers when they were affected by disease (Paddle 2012). Because they travel long distances quietly hunting small prey across large foraging territories they are rarely encountered. Because of their ancient genetic diversity, they are able to survive with minimal numbers of individuals very thinly spread across the countryside. This is the only reasonable explanation for the many sighting reports but complete lack of physical evidence.

In conclusion, we can tell when an animal is extinct; there are no more sighting reports of it. We can be sure that the Tasmanian emu is extinct, no one ever reports seeing one. There are no reports coming in of all the other unique animals that European activity has exterminated. No reports of eastern hare wallabies, toolache wallabies, no reports of paradise parrots, no reports of any of the giant marsupials that became extinct before European settlement. We will know when the Thylacine has really gone extinct; there will be no further reports of it either.

~~~

Gary Opit is the wildlife consultant for ABC North Coast Radio, and has been receiving listeners' calls and identifying animals since 1997. He works as an environmental consultant and has a field research career spanning 40 years working throughout NSW, Queensland, Papua New Guinea and South East Asia conducting vegetation and fauna survey techniques, plant identification, and identification and ecology of terrestrial vertebrate fauna.

References

Bailey, C. 2001, *Tiger Tales: Stories of the Tasmanian Tiger,* HarperCollins *Publishers* (Australia) Pty Limited.

Boness, L 2011 *Science Illustrated.* Thylacine Jaws Linked to its Extinction. Retrieved 20/09/11 from http://scienceillustrated.com.au/blog/nature/Thylacines-jaws-linked-to-its-extinction

Douglas, A. M. 1990. The Thylacine: a case for current existence on mainland Australia, Cryptozoology Interdisciplinary Journal of the International Society of Cryptozoology, 9, 13-25.

Figueiredo, B. and Janis, C. 2011, *Biology Letters.* The predatory behaviour of the Thylacine: Tasmanian tiger or marsupial wolf? Retrieved 13/03/13 http://rsbl.royalsocietypublishing.org/content/early/2011/04/29/rsbl.2011.0364

Guiler, E. 1985, *Thylacine, The Tragedy of the Tasmanian Tiger*, Oxford, Melbourne.

Guiler, E. & Godard, P. 1998, *Tasmanian Tiger, A lesson to be learned.* Abrolhos Publishing Pty Ltd, Perth, Western Australia.

Hall, P., Yaun D. and Gilmont, N. 1988, 'Mystery Animal', *Numinbah Valley, a Social and Natural History 1840's to 1988*, pp. 20, The Numinbah Valley Bicentennial Committee, 'Bonnie Doon' Numinbah Valley via Nerang, Gold Coast, Queensland.

Lentz, C., 1967, 'Hinterland Tiger Cats' *Gold Coast Bulletin*, Friday 22 September 1967 and in his memoirs published in the *Hinterlander* newspaper in 1984.

Martin, R. 1999, Land of the Longtails, *Australia Nature* magazine, Vol. 26. No. 5, winter, Australia Museum Trust, Sydney.

Paddle, R. 2000 *The Last Tasmanian Tiger, The History and Extinction of the Thylacine,* Cambridge University Press, UK.

Paddle, R. 2012. The Thylacine's last straw: epidemic disease in recent mammalian extinction, *Australian Zoologist* 36: 75-93, Royal Zoological Society of New South Wales.

Smith, D. and Macey, R. 02/03/2005, Genuine Thylacine spotters earn their stripes, Sydney Morning Herald.

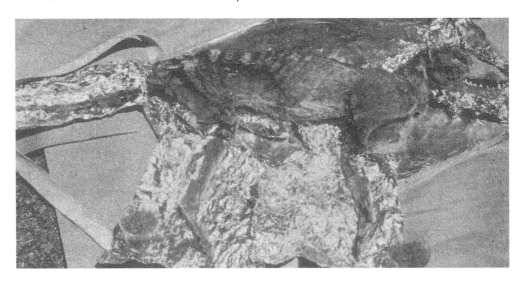

This Thylacine carcass was discovered by Jacky and David Lowry deep in a cave on the Nullarbor Plains, Western Australia in 1966. The Lowrys were exploring one of the many limestone caves in the Eucla basin when they discovered the carcass, which was remarkably well preserved and still had most of its skin and hair intact when they found the specimen. *Courtesy Western Australian Museum.*

CHAPTER 8

The Truth About the Nullarbor Thylacine

by Michael Williams

Arguably one of the most exciting Thylacine discoveries ever made has to be the October 1966 discovery of what appeared to be a fresh Thylacine carcass down a hole on the Nullarbor Plains of mainland Australia. The famous treeless landscape stretches for 1100km east-west across the state of Western Australia, its limestone foundations honeycombed with caves that have become rich pickings for scientists in search of fossilised animal remains. Those same caves have also preserved some of Australia's best examples of extinct species.

Cave explorers David and Jackie Lowry's 1966 chance discovery was full of promise and, buoyed by the support of leading West Australian zoologist Athol Douglas, they initially had every reason to believe the find could eventually re-write the Thylacine's history on the mainland and support the argument for survival of the species.

Douglas was the zoologist for the Western Australian Museum in Perth during the 1950s and '60s, and sincerely believed that the animal had died fairly recently. Douglas keenly believed in the Thylacine's continuing existence on the mainland, and would later play a role in publicising photographs of an alleged Thylacine by Kevin Cameron, which he published with his analysis in a 1986 article for *New Scientist* magazine.

Eventual carbon dating of the carcass, however, focused the age of the carcass between 4000-5000 years of age, not the 100 years that had been the original speculative guess by Douglas and the Lowrys.

Regardless, the discovery quickly attracted the attention of leading scientists and museums.

Perhaps because the hard data of this case was not circulated as widely as the speculations of Douglas at the time, the case developed its own mythos and over the years has been touted by some as 'proof positive' of mainland Thylacine survival.

Mainland Thylacine Extinctions

The most credible version of the Thylacine's technical demise on the Australian mainland occurred about 3000 years ago. According to leading scientists, among them Tim Flannery and Stephen Wroe, it was the dingo, introduced some 3500 years ago, that drove the both the Thylacine and the Tasmanian devil to extinction on mainland Australia. (1)

That the wily *Canis lupus dingo* should best the fearsomely named Tasmanian Tiger should perhaps not be so surprising.

Albert Le Souef, curator of Taronga Park Zoo, might have been seen to speculate as much when he wrote in 1923: 'When animals of this class (marsupials) suddenly find themselves placed in competition with such advanced forms as the Fox, the Cat, and the Rabbit - types far ahead of them on the evolutionary scale - it is ...inevitable that they should go down before the invader.'

Before it disappeared, the Thylacine was known to range across the Australian mainland and as far north as Papua New Guinea. Its presence so far north was first detected in 1960 with the discovery of a partial jawbone at Kiowa, which was dated to the Pleistocene era (spanning from 2.5 million to 11,700 years ago).

The dingo, Australia's largest terrestrial predator, is also implicated in the Thylacine's extinction because of a correlation between its introduction and the demise of two other vertebrates, the Tasmanian Devil and the Tasmanian native hen. (4)(5)(6) These three species all vanished from the Australian mainland during the late Holocene period, yet survived in Tasmania, due primarily to the absence of the dingo.

A sub-species of the grey wolf, the dingo was, as Le Souef pointed out above, a marsupial's worst nightmare – evolutionarily leaps and bounds ahead of its awkward convergent cousin. The fate of the Thylacine had been sealed on the mainland.

The Thylacine Hole Discovery

In October 1966 Jacky and David Lowry were exploring one of the numerous limestone caves in the Eucla basin when they discovered the carcass of a Thylacine, remarkably well preserved with most of its skin and hair intact. The carcass had been preserved due to a combination of rapid desiccation, and a lack of weathering and scavengers.

The cave, now nicknamed 'Thylacine Hole', is located 68 miles west of Eucla, on Mundrabilla station, approximately 12 miles north-west of the homestead. It has a vertical entrance shaft (1 metre), is 3 feet to 6 feet (1.8 metres) in diameter and 7 metres (25 feet) across. The cave is roughly L-shaped and about 152 metres (500 feet) across.

The cave appears to have acted as an animal trap, given the great difficulty any animal would have had in climbing back out. The smells from the decaying carcasses of the cave's victims may have attracted large numbers of carnivores to their death.

Large amounts of owl pellet deposits were found near the entrance, and 30 metres inside the entrance lay the remains of snakes, lizards, birds, rodents, a cat and several dogs (dingoes, perhaps?), rabbits, possums, kangaroos, native cats, a Tasmanian devil, and Thylacines.

Of great significance was the recovery of five other Thylacine skulls, some of which had fairly complete post-cranial parts.

The most important find of course was the remains of a well-preserved carcass of a Thylacine, which was found about 137 metres (450 feet) from the entrance on top of a rock pile. The animal was lying on its right side with its head raised off the ground.

Soft tissue had decomposed to a tarry substance that coated the exposed bones. During the initial handling of the carcass the legs broke rather easily at the joints. Even though the musty odour of decomposition was noticeable the tongue and left eyeball was still recognizable. The tail was lying about a third of a metre away (1foot).

The authors of the original paper initially speculated, pre-radiocarbon dating, of an age range from less than one year to 2000 years.

Thylacines from the Nullarbor Plain and south-western Australia are generally smaller than those from Tasmania and the eastern states. (15) Radio carbon date determinations were made on about 18 grams of the hair, desiccated skin, muscle and tissue. The results came in three years after the initial discovery and the samples came from underneath specimen F 6364 in Thylacine Hole, and clearly represented parts of F 6364 since no other source lay any where within 33 metres (100 feet).

The dates were 4,650+ or - 104,4,550+-112 and 4,650+-153 years. (17)

A dog carcass found 70 metres (200 feet) from F 6463, which appeared to be less preserved than the Thylacine carcass, was initially thought to be older but desiccated tissue gave a radio carbon date of 2,200+-96. This reinforced the idea that state of preservation is not a reliable indicator of age.

To check the reliability of these dates, D. Merrilees from the Western Australian Museum produced a paper in 1970 (18) that mentioned tests on desiccated rabbit (specimen 68.11.117) flesh, which came back 180+-76 years B.P. (Before Present, in this case meaning A.D. 1950).

The radio carbon date was increased by 3 per cent (to allow for recent redetermination of the half life of C-14 and 'reported errors are increased if necessary to a minimum of 100 years to take account of greater accuracy in laboratory measurement than warranted by general uncertainties applying to the method…and taking two standard deviations (twice the reported error) before and after the reported date'. This meant rabbit specimen 68.11.117 probably died between A.D. 1565 to A.D 1950.

Contamination by radioactively 'dead' carbon in the Limestone dust stuck to the rabbit specimen, and Thylacine for that matter, cannot account for the possibility of an earlier age (before 1895) since both specimens were treated with hydrochloric acid. This opened up (according to D. Merrilees) the slim (and novel) possibility rabbits might have been introduced into Australia by the survivors from the Dutch vessel *Vergulden Draak*, wrecked in Western Australia in 1656. (19)

Merrilees concluded 'if the radiocarbon age estimate on desiccated rabbit tissue is of the right order, it seems likely that similar estimates on similar materials from other mammals in the same locality are also of the right order'.

Jacky and David Lowrys' thoughts

The following comments were received via personal communications with the Lowrys during 2013.

David Lowry's first thought on seeing the Thylacine carcass was 'what is this funny dingo with stripes?' It was his wife Jacky who had to tell him about Thylacines and why their discovery of the carcass was so important.

'I had grown up in New Zealand and came to Western Australia as a field geologist for the WA Geological Survey in 1962. Four years later I still had a fair bit to learn about Australia,' David said.

His wife Jacky can clearly recall her first view of the Thylacine. 'It was a long way from the entrance, near a wall, and the roof was low. I had to crawl to approach the carcass, and my approach was towards the head. The convergent evolution of the dog and the Thylacine had been an example in my studies, so I was aware of the differences, as well as the similarities between them. One of the first things I noticed was the wide zygomatic arch, quite different from a dog skull, so I was already alerted to the possibility that this was a marsupial. The stripes on the back was another alert. I knew that dogs had four incisors, Thylacines six, so one of the first things I did was to count them.

'It was very, very exciting. I remember counting along one jaw, getting to three and thinking, "This can't be true!" and counting again to be certain. "My goodness, it must be true! "And counting again. "Wow, it is true!" By then we had already found the other skulls closer to the entrance, so the idea that we had a Thylacine was not exceptional. It was its remarkable state of preservation. There was even a slight musty smell.'

David's initial thought was that the carcass could only be a few tens of years old, and this was also the impression of Duncan Merrilees, paleontologist at the Museum who was doing a Ph.D. on Australia's faunal extinctions. 'In our 1967 paper (prior to the carbon dating results) we noted "speculative estimates of the age of the carcass range from less than one year to 2000 years".'

'I don't recall thinking about the age,' Jacky said, 'but I do remember the carcass's brittleness, and the tarry nature of the gums, and the reddish stains on bone. That was quite different from the carcass and bones closer to the entrance; all indicators of age. The fur was rather tatty.'

George Kendrick from the Western Australian Museum, and Tony Cockbain (G.S.W.A.), drove out with a special box to transport the carcass back to Perth.

'Duncan was very excited and wanted to have the Nullarbor declared a Thylacine reserve,' David said. 'The night Jacky and I got back to Perth, we were asked to attend an exhibition opening at the Museum where the carcass would be shown to the Governor. The Governor peered at it and remarked, "they could be alive out there today". Duncan reckoned his Thylacine reserve was off to a good start. Luckily the reserve never eventuated because I needed to continue field work on the Nullarbor and the pastoralists would have been furious.'

'When the carbon dating results came back, the significance changed from "perhaps they are still alive" to "what remarkable preservation." I have not seen Athol Douglas's original comments on possible contamination – only what gets recycled on various websites. I find the concept inconceivable. It would be possible for contamination by fallen limestone fragments, but one of the three samples was treated with acid to remove this possibility.

'It is easy for a trace of modern carbon to make ancient carbon (more than about 30,000 years) look a bit younger, but it is hard to make young carbon look old. The half-life of Carbon14 is 5,730 years. Roughly speaking, the age determinations of 4,650, 4,550, 4,650 before present (1950) would have been calculated because the Thylacine material had only about half the modern amount of C14 (relative to the common stable C12). To get modern Thylacine material to look 4600-years-old would require replacing half the sample with ancient carbon. I find this inconceivable.

'One website mentioning Athol Douglas says "that method of dating may be invalid since the body had been soaking in groundwater." This is rubbish. The cave was particularly dry and no water had been anywhere near the carcass. In fact, the cave had a lot of salt (halite). I first recognised halite in Mullamullang Cave. To the best of my knowledge halite had never been recorded before in a limestone cave. It occurs because of the extreme dryness. Nullarbor caves are very dry, and the Thylacine Hole particularly so. Water enters the entrance shaft when it rains, and there are some areas with a flat clay floor showing that water had pooled, but it is probably ancient – there was bone material on top but none in the clay.'

David recalled speculating that the light powdering of halite on much of the clay floor may have deterred the hair-eating beetles from reaching the carcass.

'My memory suggests the Thylacine carcass was found at a higher elevation than the lowest parts where water could pool,' Jacky said.

'I think the greater distance of the Thylacine carcass from the entrance may have been a factor in limiting the number of flies and dermestids to reach it, hence the presence of fur. Modern carcasses near the entrance had tight, fur-less skin stretched over bones. I remember one modern kangaroo carcass that had masses of fly larval cases spilling, as it were, all over it and around it. In contrast, there were very few fly larval cases around the carcass.

'I'm not sure that a light powdering of halite would have deterred flies and dermestids from "reaching" the carcass. They can fly. Once there, a powdering of halite might have deterred them from eating the carcass, but I don't think so. Flies are interested in a carcass almost immediately, and dermestids come into the picture pretty promptly as well. Perhaps moths too. It would have taken time for a light powdering of halite to develop; I suspect too long to function as a deterrent for ravaging insects. However, if a light powdering of halite did develop (I don't think anyone has ever checked), it would possibly help in preservation.'

The beliefs of Athol Douglas

Athol Douglas was Senior Experimental Officer at the Western Australian Museum, Perth. And Douglas was adamant that the Thylacine Hole carcass had to be of a recent age, which implied the initial radio-carbon results and subsequent verification were essentially wrong: 'I am not convinced that the carbon-14 dating is completely reliable. In Limestone caves there is always the possibility of pollution by waters containing carbon from distant sources...I have examined the Mundrabilla Thylacine where it is preserved at the western Australian Museum...it is a dried out hollow shell, with no skin or hair on the underside. It is at the stage of decomposition where the action of bacteria and maggots has ceased...these remains are then attacked by the larvae of dermestid and trogid beetles and certain moths. Parts of the pads, the nose and areas of the tail had been very obviously attacked by dermestid larvae, which often favour the base of the tail because there is so much sinew there. These recycling agents would surely have destroyed the carcass by now if it were 4000 years old.' (20)

The possible contamination as well as insect damage was more than adequately dealt with by David Lowry in his response.

I can find no references to any objection Douglas might have had (must have had) to the paper by Merrilees (18) on the follow up radiocarbon dates.

Douglas also appears to have believed that someone had interfered with the Thylacine specimen by placing it on a recent rock fall pile. (20)

To be fair, the views of Douglas at the time have to been seen in some form of context. The Douglas article (21) was produced to discuss the photographs presented to Douglas by Kevin Cameron in February 1985, which appear to show a Thylacine with its head down a hole.

Douglas (by implication) had also shown the photos to Dr Ronald Strahan, a zoologist at the Australian Museum who disagreed with Douglas' ultimate identification.

In the *New Scientist* article, Douglas talks about Cameron's photos, which he obviously believes are real. He then tries to bolster his case for the veracity of the Cameron photos by seguing to discuss the Thylacine Hole carcass.

At a later date he wrote: 'When I saw the negatives, I realised Cameron's account with regard to the photographs was inaccurate. The film had been cut, frames were missing, and the photos were taken from different angles - making it impossible for the series to have been taken in 20 or 30 seconds, as Cameron had stated. Furthermore, in one negative, there was the shadow of another person pointing what could be an over-under 12 gauge shotgun.'

'Cameron had told me he had been alone. It would have been practically impossible for an animal as alert as a Thylacine to remain stationary for so long while human activity was going on in its vicinity. In addition, it is significant that the animal's head does not appear in any of the photographs.' (20)

Without having the negatives to examine, and working off the initial photos, the time sequence, judging by the shadow lines, falls apart. An Internet forum poster (I realise the dubious nature of this reference) who claimed to have been a relative of Cameron's has also claimed that Kevin waited for the animal to return that day, and managed to photograph it in the same position again, however this seems implausible.

Why Douglas never noticed the problem with the shadows and original claims just from looking at the prints prior to publishing the article in *New Scientist*, until after others criticised the photos, is not explained. There was also a photo used in the *New Scientist* article that showed a gun in the foreground. How Cameron managed to hold a gun and take the photo was not explained.

The Sydney Morning Herald interviewed Athol Douglas in July 1986. Douglas explained that he had recently directed several questions to Cameron's solicitor. The questions were: Who processed the film? Was Cameron accompanied by anyone else? At what time of day and over what time span were they taken? Was the Thylacine alive in all the photos, and if not, where is the carcass? Cameron declined to respond to the questions. (22).

Why these most basic of questions were never asked nor clarified in the first 20 minutes of seeing the photos is never explained.

Conclusion

This brief segue into the claims of Douglas regarding the photos of Cameron is justified for several reasons. I could not obtain a copy of the relevant edition of Cryptozoology (20) and the only reference I could find to this article was on the internet, which extrapolated a few lines of what Douglas supposedly believed: 'Douglas (1990) also notes that the layer of limestone rubble on which the specimen was found was the result of a very recent rock fall from the ceiling, and he suspects that the carcass was probably placed on the rock pile by previous, unknown visitors to the cave.' (23)

Since Douglas was the only academic I am aware of that had closely examined the actual carcass and publicly argued against the dates of the death of the animal recovered from the Thylacine Hole, I had to refer to the *New Scientist* article. I am also aware of some very interesting 'recent' Thylacine sightings from WA. (24)

With fresh eyes, I realised the central weaknesses of Douglas article on Cameron's photos, as well as problems with his conclusions regarding the Thylacine carcass at the museum. This is not to malign his work as a scientist or to attack him personally or to impugn his integrity in any way, shape or form. However, it shows clearly that when confronted with unusual claims (Cameron's photos) followed by a strong desire to bolster one's case, we can all fall into a trap and suspend our critical abilities. And in that regard, academics are no different to anyone else.

I willingly admit my own enthusiasm for this discovery was based around the initial belief that, given enough research into this case, I would be able to find supporting proof and accept the conclusions of Athol Douglas.

When I started writing this article, I seriously believed the current meme among many 'cryptozoology enthusiasts', which was that the Thylacine carcass from Thylacine Hole, was of a relatively recent age. By this, I mean I initially believed it probably died within approximately the past 100 years.

This was based on what little I knew about the discovery, as well as from a casual reading of the objections of Athol Douglas to the carbon dating times. Over several months, and following personal contact with David and Jacky Lowry, I have come to the opposite conclusion and now believe the dating and conclusions are correct.

The 'Thylacine in the hole' is old bones – very old bones – but its discovery has helped to inform scientists about what we know of the mainland Thylacine: its size, appearance, range, and diet.

Intriguingly there are still reports of Thylacines seen on the Nullarbor, but nothing as compelling as the Thylacine in the Hole has ever been found since the Lowrys made their chance discovery.

Perhaps somewhere in that vast expanse *is* proof of a species living on the edge, evading the snapping jaws of antipodean wolves, but unfortunately this isn't it.

~~~

*Michael Williams has spent the past 20 years investigating strange events and mystery animal sightings across Australia and South East Asia. He is the co-author with Rebecca Lang of **Australian Big Cats: An Unnatural History of Panthers**, which pieced together the legend of Australia's mysterious 'black panther', and co-wrote the foreword for **Savage Shadow: The Hunt for the Australian Cougar**. His work has been featured in various media and documentaries including the Discovery Channel's Animal X series, and 'Prints of Darkness', about inexplicable sightings of large black cats in New Zealand. Since 2013 he has been undertaking expeditions to Tasmania in search of irrefutable evidence of the Thylacine.*

References

1. An Explorer's Notebook: Essays on Life, History and Climate By Tim Flannery 2007

2. Smith, M. 1982 Review of the Thylacine (Marsupialia, Thylacinidae). In Carnivorous marsupials (ed. M. Archer), pp. 237 – 253. Sydney, Australia: Royal Zoological Societyof New South Wales, Surrey.

3. Johnson, C. N. & Wroe, S. 2003 Causes of extinction of vertebrates during the Holocene of mainland Australia: Arrival of the dingo, or human impact? Holocene 13,941 – 948.4/The predatory behaviour of the Thylacine - published online 4 May 2011.

Biol. Lett.Borja Figueirido and Christine M. Janis

4. Archer, M. 1974: New information about the Quaternary distribution of the Thylacine (Marsupialia, Thylacinidae) in Australia. Journal of the Royal Society Of Western Australia.

5. Baird, R.F. The dingo as a possible factor in the disappearance of Gallinula mortierii from the Australian mainland. The Emu 91,121–22

6. Corbett, L. 1995: The dingo in Australia and Asia. Sydney: University of NSW Press.

7. Tasmanian devil (*Sarcophilus harrisii*) extinction on the Australian mainland in the mid-Holocene: multi-causality and ENSO intensification Alcheringa: An Australasian Journal of Palaeontology Volume 30, Supplement 1, 2006

8. Partridge J (1967) A 3,300 year old Thylacine (Marsupialia: Thylacinidae) from the

Nullarbor Plain, Western Australia. J R Soc West Aust 50: 57-59.

9. Medlin GC (1996) Report on vertebrate remains from a sinkhole in the Venus Bay Conservation Park. South Australia. Adelaide: Department of Environment and Natural Resources.

10. Smith M (1982) Review of the Thylacine. In: Archer M, editor. Carnivorous Marsupials. Mosman: Royal Zoological Society of New South Wales. pp. 257-253.

11. Macintosh NWG, Mahoney JA (1964) A 4,000 years old Thylacine tooth (Dasyuridae) from Shelter 2. Proc R Soc Vic 77: 507-516

12. Gale SJ (2009) Event chronostratigraphy: A high-resolution tool for dating the recent past. Quat Geochronol 4: 391-399.

13. Merrilees D (1970) A check on the radiocarbon dating of desiccated Thylacine (marsupial "wolf") and dog tissue from Thylacine Hole, Nullarbor Region, Western Australia. Helictite 8: 39-42.

14. Archer M (1974) New information about the Quaternary distribution of the Thylacine (Marsupialia, Thylacinidae) in Australia. J R Soc West Aust 57: 43-49.

15. RIDE, W. D. L., 1964. A review of Australian fossil marsupials. Presidential Address, 1963. J. Roy. Soc. W. Aust. 47: 97-131.

16. Discovery of a Thylacine (Tasmanian Tiger) Carcass in a Cave Near Eucla, Western Australia. Lowry, David C &Lowry, Jacoba W. J. Lowry Vol 5, No 2, January, 1967 Helictite

17. Lowry, J.W.J. and D. Merrilees. 1969. Age of the desiccated carcass of a Thylacine (Marsupialia, Dasyuroidea) from Thylacine Hole, Nullarbor Region, Western Australia. Helictite 7:15–16.

18. D.Merrilees. A check on the radiocarbon dating of desiccated Thylacine (Marsupial 'wolf') and dog tissue from Thylacine Hole, Nullarbor region Western Australia. Helictite Vol8.No 2. April 1970, page 39

19. J.E.Heere 1606-1765 The part borne by the Dutch in the discovery of Australia, Luaz, London

20. DOUGLAS, A. M., 1990. The Thylacine: a case for current existence on mainland Australia. Cryptozoology, 9, pp. 13-25.

21. Athol Douglas: Tigers In Western Australia. New Scientist, 24 April 1986.

22. The Sydney Morning herald-July 29-1986-Colour Photos of Tasmanian Tiger Doubted.

23. www.naturalworlds.org/Thylacine/palaeontology/prehistoric/ prehistoric_range_4.htm

24. Heberle-2004-Reports of alleged Thylacine sightings in Western Australia-Conservation Science Western Australia 5 (1) 1-5-2004

A captive male Thylacine asleep at the Domain Zoo in Hobart, Tasmania, taken circa 1927-1929. *Courtesy of the Queen Victoria Museum.*

CHAPTER 9

Scientists and the Construction of the Thylacine's Extinction

by Dr Robert Paddle

The cultural and biological pattern of extinction in Australia, following the waves of human invasions from Asia, South East Asia and, finally, Europe, parallel the history of biodiversity reduction experienced on other continents. Extinctions automatically followed the original spread of the human species out of its evolutionary home in Africa, a process that has been hastened more recently, through the economic imperative associated with European colonisation.

Extinction is a continuing and present reality, reflected in the dominant cultural climate and economic values of the Australian community, which urgently needs to be addressed in the degraded, contemporary Australian environment, through direct social and political action. All too often, rather than taking the scientific and lay communities unawares, extinction is frequently known, expected and predicted well in advance of its occurrence. For example, the endling representative of the toolache wallaby (*Macropus greyi*) of south-eastern South Australia and south-western Victoria, died in captivity in a private animal collection at Robe, South Australia, on 30 June 1939, 51 years after its extinction was predicted by the Native Fauna and Flora Protection Committee of the Field Naturalist's Society of the Royal Society of South Australia (1888).

At the time of the last major human invasion of Australia, an intellectual recognition of the reality of extinction already existed within the arriving European culture. Thanks to Georges Cuvier and his detailed fossil reconstructions of the European *Mastodon* and South American *Megatherium* in the late 18th century, the existence of extinction was not an issue. However, the causes of extinction remained the subject of heated intellectual debate – with fossils seen as either the antediluvian remnants of a spiritually-ordained global flooding, only a few millennia old, or, alternatively, as the natural products of geological and biological processes operating over increasingly longer periods of time. But as far as 17th and 18th-century perceptions of extinction were concerned, no debate was needed for the existence of a third possible cause of extinction, namely the intrusive and destructive effects of the invasive human species, as exemplified in the widely-known extinction of the dodo (*Raphus cucullatus*) from the island of Mauritius in the 1680s.

With the European discovery of the Thylacine and its eventual classification, initially as *Didelphis cynocephalus* (Harris, 1808) the Thylacine was formally introduced to the scientific community, and to scientific methodology.

The core construct behind being a scientist is that you take your idea, equation or hypothesis and test it. But not against current knowledge or data. (If your idea, equation or hypothesis does not appear to be right at the time of its conception; does not appear to conform with current perceptual reality then, whatever you are, you are certainly not a scientist.) A scientist takes that idea, equation or hypothesis and tests it against new data. The said process of testing it is not, however, one of seeking confirmation, but rather an intellectual attempt to disprove the idea, equation or hypothesis. With disproof as the core of scientific methodology, comes the importance, to the scientist, of being wrong. As expressed by T.H. Huxley, "Next to being right in this world, the best of all things is to be clearly and definitely wrong" (cited in Routh, 1902 p393), which encompasses the principle of attempting to disprove predicted scientific hypotheses; and only with the failure to consistently disprove an hypothesis, at an acceptable level or acceptable number of times, is it appropriate to consider that the original predicted hypothesis has been supported, and may indeed, turn out to be "right", and be granted the highest scientific status of being a theory.[18] Hence the ultimate importance, to any scientist, of being wrong.

With the identification and classification of an antipodean marsupial wolf (Owen, 1842), European scientists were quick to predict its likely extinction. As expressed by

---

[18] Significant differences between the vulgar and professional usage of the word "theory" need to be acknowledged. The theory of evolution stands side-by-side with the theory of gravity. The intellectual denial of evolution as an influential factor in our past, present and future experiences as an individual (or species), is no more tenable than the intellectual denial of gravity as an influential factor in our past, present and future experiences as an individual (or species). Both are theories, scientific statements capable of disproof, but nobody has managed to do so as yet. If one is to remain in contact with perceptual reality the existence of evolution and gravity need acknowledgement in our everyday life and actions.

Richard Owen, "the thylacine ... soon is likely to be, extinct" (1843, p149), and, as concluded by John Gould, in time, the Thylacine will "become entirely extinct" (1851 – the original date of publication, although frequently identified in the modern literature by its republication date of 1863). (Laplace's possible prediction of extinction in 1835 predates both of the above, but as identified in the excellent historical analysis of the Thylacine by Freeman [2010, p67] there is some confusion as to whether, with his "chien du diable", he was referring to the extinction of the Thylacine, or, alternatively, the Tasmanian devil.)

Owen's hypothesised extinction for the Thylacine was based upon the premise that "if it looks like a member of the wolf family (the Canidae) it will probably be treated as if it were a member of the wolf family", and his contemporary knowledge of both the extermination of the insular European populations of the placental wolf (*Canis lupus*), as well as the continuing destruction directed at the species on the continental landmass itself. In constructing this parallel Owen had only half the picture, as his fellow scientist, Charles Darwin, was still immersed in the 20-plus years he spent testing his hypothesis of natural selection (resulting in descent with modification, now formally known as evolution).

Darwin was not simply seeking out confirmatory instances from natural history fields supporting evolution (a valuable first step, but essentially a non-experimental approach, one that was later hit upon by Alfred Russel Wallace), but by attempting to test his evolutionary hypothesis against newly constructed data. First, he set out to become the world's acknowledged authority on living and fossil barnacles (producing four monographs thereon in the early 1850s), and testing every new fact he discovered in this new field of research, as a potential refutation or challenge to his hypothesised natural selection; and, secondly, seeking evolution's laboratory testing by examining the history and practice of animal and plant domestication, with its establishment of different breed and variety types, through artificial selection, and experimenting in that field himself.

By 1850, the European scientific expectation of the Thylacine's extinction had moved from the pages of scientific publication to that of the popular press: "these rare animals [thylacines]... are now rapidly disappearing" (*Times*, 21/5/1850).

The Tasmanian scientist, Ronald Campbell Gunn, preceded his European counterparts in predicting extinction (in unpublished correspondence at the time), not just on the basis of placental wolf parallels, but also with the added impetus of another Tasmanian extinction that would precede that of the Thylacine. The first large and significant vertebrate species that obviously became extinct to the resident

European population was the Tasmanian emu (*Dromaius diemenensis*). The Tasmanian emu was not uncommon in the eastern half of Tasmania in 1804, was rare by 1830, and became extinct during the early 1850s. The two emus donated by James Gibson of Circular Head, that formed part of the first recorded display of animals in the Launceston City Park in 1850, appear to be the last known representatives of the species (*Launceston Cornwall Chronicle*, 24/10/1850).[19] Adam Amos (letter, 20/4/1826, cited in Barrett, 1944, p132) penned an early warning from Oyster Bay: "there is a kind of ostrich. We have only caught one. I believe they will soon be extinct". In a letter to William Hooker in 1836, Gunn outlined the unsuccessful attempt he had made to get Lieutenant-Governor Arthur to respond to the plight and likely extinction of a number of significant representatives of Tasmania's fauna, mentioning the emu's problem in particular:

Many of our animals and Birds will become extinct … Emus are now extremely rare – and in a few years will be quite gone … a few pounds employed in collecting emus … would have been no great matter and their food, being grass alone, no expense would have been incurred beyond fencing in a piece of ground. (Gunn, letter 16/11/1836). When Lieutenant-Governor Arthur refused the minimal economic request, of setting aside and fencing a few acres of Tasmanian grassland, in order to prevent the extinction of the Tasmanian emu, he set a cultural precedent all too readily followed by succeeding generations of Australian administrators, bureaucrats and politicians.

---

[19] Le Souëf (1907, p180) suggested the Tasmanian emu only became extinct in the 1880s, and the *Launceston Daily Telegraph* (27/7/1923) later gave the specific date of extinction as 1873. However, occasional attempts were made by private individuals and institutions to introduce and acclimatise into Tasmania the mainland species of emu *D. novaehollandiae*. There were mainland emus on display in a purpose-built enclosure in the menagerie in Launceston City Park in 1869, and a concerted, but ultimately unsuccessful effort to acclimatise the mainland emu was made by a group of individuals in the 1880s (Jenkins, 1977, p94), one of whom, Mr J. Syme of Hobart, donated three mainland emus to the Launceston City Park Zoo in 1886 (*Launceston Examiner*, 29/11/1886). The last specimens of these unsuccessful acclimatisation attempts, observed either in the wild, or in captivity at Launceston City Park Zoo, are the probable source for suggestions that Tasmanian emus were still in existence in the 1870s and 1880s. Which represents an early illustration of the important principle argued herein, that sightings of a supposedly extinct animal, in themselves, cannot be considered as evidence for the continued existence of that species. Only evidence provided that is capable of scientific analysis, testing and experimentation can overturn a designation of extinction.

Gunn made further unpublished intimations of Tasmanian vertebrate extinctions (letter 31/3/1937), specifically mentioning the Thylacine: "In a very few years this Animal [the Thylacine] so highly interesting to the Zoologist will be extinct" (draft manuscript 1850), a perspective finally published, with similar prediction by Gunn in 1852 (although frequently identified in the modern literature as being written by the editor of the publication, John West).

As Secretary of, and an active presenter of papers to, the Tasmanian Society, Gunn's views were widely known to the scientific community, and the likely extinction of significant elements of Tasmania's indigenous fauna was aired in the popular press:

> In a few years the changes introduced by civilisation will have obliterated many interesting, natural and physical records, [and will] have placed many of the "feroe naturæ" on the list of those already, from various causes, utterly destroyed, the whole race forever gone, lost to the naturalist and the world. (*Hobarton Guardian*, 23/9/1848).

Unquestionably, by the middle of the 19th century, Tasmanian and European scientists, as well as the literate and educated public on both sides of the world, were well aware of the potential extinction of indigenous, Tasmanian species. Yet the stark reality is, for all the knowledge and interest possessed at the time, it was not good enough.

In November 1836 Gunn floated the idea of the possible extinction of the Thylacine. But come the New Year of 1837, the Thylacine was still demonstrably in existence, and Gunn was demonstrably wrong. The same was true for 1838, 1839 and 1840; Gunn was demonstrably wrong again. In fact, Gunn was demonstrably wrong for the next 100 years (save two months), until the endling of the species died in Hobart Zoo during the night of 7 September 1936. Gunn was demonstrably wrong for a century, but in reality, he was wrong for the right reasons. The very opposite occurred just five months later in February 1937, when the Tasmanian Animals and Birds Protection Board, through both radio broadcast and newspaper publication suggested the Thylacine was extinct:

> Members of the Animals and Birds Protection Board are concerned lest the Tasmanian Thylacinus (native tiger) should have become extinct. Reliable data indicates that it is some years since the last tiger was seen in the State ... it is feared that the animal ... may have ceased to exist ... We have no reliable evidence of the present existence anywhere of these animals ... we do not know that the animal is not extinct. (*Hobart Mercury*, 10/2/1937)

Not that they meant it, however. The published declaration of extinction was merely thrown out as a challenge to the general Tasmanian public to prove them wrong. (In this, it must be said, it has to date proved to be spectacularly unsuccessful.) But the Board's actual opinion was otherwise to the spin that was expressed in its public position. As the Board explained to a concerned Society for the Preservation of the Fauna of the Empire: "While the Thylacinus has undoubtedly become scarce, the Tasmanian Board does not fear that the animal has yet become extinct" (Secretary, Animals and Birds Protection Board, letter 25/3/1938). The Tasmanian Fauna Board's declaration of the Thylacine's extinction in February 1937 turned out to be demonstrably right, but in reality, it was a case of being right for the wrong reasons.

During the 100 years during which Gunn's prediction of the Thylacine's extinction was wrong, Darwin finally concluded his initial research and published his scientific demonstration of the reality of evolution, with *On the Origin of Species* (1859). In this monograph Darwin identified the existence of evolutionary convergence, expressed in the following manner (including a subtle allusion to Alfred Russel Wallace whilst so doing):

> I am inclined to believe that in nearly the same way as two men have sometimes independently hit on the very same invention, so natural selection, working for the good of each being and taking advantage of analogous variations, has sometimes modified in very nearly the same manner two parts in two organic beings, which owe but little of their structure in common to inheritance from the same ancestor. (1859, pp193-194)

With the recognition of evolutionary convergence the missing half of Owen's original argument was now available: 'If it looks like a member of the wolf family (the Canidae) it will probably behave as if it were a member of the wolf family.' A proposition significantly confirmed in 19th century records of the Thylacine's behaviour (from both Indigenous and European sources), which identify the Thylacine as living and co-operatively hunting in small family groups, within an established home range or territory - such conformity challenging more recent 20th century records and collected observations of the species' behaviour (Paddle, 2000).

Of course, given that the accepted definition of extinction is the absence of evidence for 50 years, one could argue that Gunn's prediction of extinction was actually wrong for the next 150 years (to 7 September 1986), at which date the Thylacine became officially extinct, with the extinction event backdated 50 years. This 50-year definition of extinction, developed in the latter half of the 20th century, was originally a product of deliberations by the International Council for Bird Preservation; that received widespread support through its use in the *Convention on International Trade in Endangered Species of Wild Flora and Fauna*, and its adoption by the International Union for Conservation of Nature.

Once this definition is applied to specific species, it becomes an hypothesis, leading to the specific conclusion of relevance here that based on knowledge-to-date, "the Thylacine is extinct". This represents a workable scientific hypothesis, one that is open to refutation, and capable of being proved wrong since 8 September 1986. It is completely appropriate for a scientist to say the Thylacine is extinct, for this conforms to current reality – no demonstrable evidence for fifty years. But having said that, it is also completely appropriate (and logical) for a scientist to take an interest in contemporary sightings of the Thylacine. This is not a case of cognitive dissonance, but merely a reflection upon scientific methodology. Post 1936, claimed instances of Thylacine encounters actually involve a testing or potential disproof of the hypothesis of extinction, and the core attempt to disprove a scientific idea, equation or hypothesis lies at the very heart of scientific endeavour.

Fortunately, post 1936, concerned Tasmanian scientists did not sit back and wait for any fifty-year criterion to be met. Lindsay Crawford, zoologist at the Queen Victoria Museum, Launceston, was the first scientist to consistently record oral history accounts of the species. He set about interviewing old-timers, bushmen and bushwomen in 1951, not just to obtain contemporary information as to the likely whereabouts of the species (data which was being collected also by the Tasmanian Animals and Birds Protection Board), but, more importantly to question and record people's memory of the behaviour of the species (Crawford, 1958).[20] In the early

---

[20] Over time, the sightings data collected by the Tasmanian Animals and Birds Protection Board have serviced numerous attempts, both by the Board and by approved, select individuals, to mount expeditions in Tasmania searching for the Thylacine. All have proved unsuccessful, with nothing more to show for their efforts than an impressive array of plaster casts of wombat footprints (Crawford, 1958).

Having raised the subject of plaster casts here, it is worth digressing to explain why plaster casts associated with claimed modern sightings of the Thylacine do not amount to definitive evidence. For rough comparative purposes, plaster casts have been made of the impressions of Thylacine feet from preserved museum specimens, but these are specimens with dried or spirit affected digital and plantar pads on the feet, often reduced in size, far harder than that to be found in the living animal, and incapable of showing the different splay of the digits in different substrates. Nobody ever made plaster casts of the tracks of a live Thylacine prior to 1937. Plaster casts associated

1960s Eric Guiler (first a member of, in 1953, and later chairman of the Tasmanian Animals and Birds Protection Board) also began interviewing trappers for their historical, first-hand accounts of the behaviour of the species (Guiler, 1985, p vii).

Twentieth-century observations of the Thylacine represent, however, observations of a species under severe social and environmental stress. Post the slaughter practised against the species through public and private bounties (the government bounty ran from 1888 to 1909 and accounted for the destruction of some 2,209 Thylacines), together with the appearance of a significant epidemic marsupi-carnivore disease around – and after - 1895 (Paddle, 2012),[21] there are few surprises that many recorded behaviours of the species in the 20th century - suggesting the Thylacine was a solitary hunter, travelling long distances, probably of no fixed abode, and with females rearing their young in isolation – contrast with behavioural records from the 19th century (Paddle, 2000).

Although the last Hobart Zoo Thylacine has been identified as the endling of the species, in reality, this is no more likely than suggesting that the most recent fossil, or sub-fossil of a species, actually represents the last living representative of that species. In themselves, fossilisation, or capture and display in a zoological garden, are rare and unlikely events for any individual within a given population of a species.

The scientific statement and hypothesis that the Thylacine is extinct, clearly allows for its refutation. Australian mammalogy provides a number of examples where the

---

with modern sightings of Thylacines may certainly be described as "interesting", but they cannot be considered as evidence for the continued existence of the species as there is no scientific database against which these modern plaster casts may be compared.

[21] The symptoms of the epidemic disease recorded in captivity (Paddle, 2012) have led to the suggestion that the disease was likely to be a lupus-like autoimmune condition associated with the stress of loss of habitat and being hunted (Selwood, letters 6/3/2012, 29/3/2012).

  I use the words "symptoms" and "epidemic" in the full knowledge that conventionally these terms are meant to be restricted to the human condition. But having spent the bulk of my academic career in psychology rather than zoology departments, in which the reality of evolution and the relatedness of all species is frequently ignored, I have become philosophically opposed to the construction or restricted use of supposedly unique human attributes or conditions, when these same attributes and conditions are shared by other animals.

designation of extinction, with its 50-year criterion, has proved incorrect. Specimens of Leadbeater's possum (*Gymnobelideus leadbeateri*) were last collected in 1909, and it was believed extinct before its rediscovery in 1961. The desert rat-kangaroo (*Caloprymnus campestris*) was first recorded in 1841, and a full 90 years elapsed before another specimen was found in 1931. (Its recovery from extinction was brief, however, as no specimens from this isolated population have been seen since 1935.)[22] Encompassing even greater time spans in an Australian context, two mammals, the northern hairy-nosed wombat (*Lasiorhinus krefftii*) and the mountain pygmy possum (*Burramys parvus*) were actually first described and named as extinct fossil specimens, before living representatives were found.

By definition, the Thylacine is extinct, and that label will remain in place until a body is produced, preferably alive, but if not, dead – and no amount of contemporary sightings are going to change that statement. This is not to suggest that contemporary sightings are without value; the number of times the 50-year criterion has already been broken clearly suggests otherwise, but Thylacine sightings, in themselves, do not have the power to overcome the definition of the species' extinction. Without an accompanying body, they cannot be used as evidence for the continued existence of the species, but being honest, such sightings may well be of great interest.

A digression first of all, towards a non-Thylacine illustration of what is meant by sightings of 'great interest'. Numerous sightings of a large, tree-climbing striped marsupial cat have been recorded from Queensland in the 19th and 20th centuries. For example:

> Up here in York Peninsula we have a tiger cat that stands as high as a hefty, medium-sized dog. His body is lithe and sleek and beautifully striped in black and grey. His pads are armed with lance-like claws of great tearing strength. His ears are sharp and pricked, and his head is shaped like that of a tiger. (Ion Idriess, cited in Le Souëf and Burrell, 1926, p330)

---

22 Scientists, like all creative artists, play with ideas. Sometimes they play with words as well. I was asked to write a review of Tim Flannery and Peter Schouten's book on extinct animals, *A Gap in Nature* (2001) – Flannery responsible for the text, Schouten the illustrations - and, in so doing, the desert rat-kangaroo provided me with the largest anagram I have constructed to date. A little archaically, the review includes the following expression "both collaborators ... enfetter *Caloprymnus* in the ranks of the extinct" (Paddle, 2002, p174). The four words commencing with "enfetter" contain all the letters of both collaborators first and second names.

Its first appearance in the scientific literature occurred with a sighting recorded by Sheridan in the *Proceedings of the Zoological Society of London* in 1871.

Such was the strength of recorded sightings and newspaper reports that, in the first attempt to produce a full species list and description of all Australian mammals, Le Souëf and Burrell gave it the status of an extant North Queensland species; albeit one awaiting formal scientific identification, classification and description; but after four pages of text they named and described it as the "striped marsupial cat" (1926, pp329-332).

> Description from field observations. Hair short, rather coarse. General colour fawn or grey, with broad black stripes on flanks, not meeting over back. Head like that of a cat; nose more pronounced. Ears sharp, pricked. Tail well haired, inclined to be tufted at the end. Feet large, claws long, sharp. Total length about five feet; height at shoulder eighteen inches. (Le Souëf and Burrell, 1926, p332)

In the next published full catalogue of Australian mammal species, the widely read and frequently revised and up-dated *Furred Animals of Australia* by Ellis Troughton (1941, pp48-50; and in all subsequent seven editions of the book produced over the following twenty years) the existence of the striped marsupial cat was also accepted as an extant species from Queensland. A knowledge of the fossil discovery of the bones of the marsupial lion *Thylacoleo carnifex* encouraged cryptozoologists to associate recorded sightings of the striped marsupial cat with the continued existence of the marsupial lion (Healy and Cropper, 1994). But, claws aside, there was little to link the bones of the scientists' marsupial lion with the claimed external appearance from recorded sightings of Queensland's striped marsupial cat. That was, however, altered with the publication of a photograph of an ancient, well-preserved, Aboriginal drawing from a rock shelter in the northern Kimberley (Akerman and Willing, 2009). Flannery's description of the artwork reads as follows:

> The marsupial lion is unmistakable … Courtesy of a careful but long-forgotten artist, we now know that it had powerful forequarters, a large box-like head with triangular ears, a long, tufted tail and an evenly striped back … its most striking feature is its extraordinarily muscular forearms, one of which is depicted crooked … ready to strike with its lethal claw. (Flannery, 2012, p49)

Nineteenth and 20th-century sightings of a striped marsupial cat, that we now know, as of 2009, bear striking parallels to the external appearance of the marsupial lion, do not amount to evidence for the continued existence of the marsupial lion in Queensland – nothing but a body could determine this - but to any stretch of the imagination, by scientists and non-scientists alike, one now is forced to admit these sightings are of "great interest".

Returning, again, to supposed sightings of the Thylacine. For a scientist, as in the reading of a (non-historical) novel, examining the evidence of a modern Thylacine sighting involves the suspension of disbelief. That said, and it being accepted as "a given", any data presented in accounts of modern Thylacine sightings, are certainly open to being tested against known data established for the species prior to 1937. Occasionally, modern Thylacine sightings involve the reporting of unusual behaviours in the animal observed; behaviours whose significance is unknown, or possibly incorrectly interpreted by the observer, yet, when tested against the scientific record, it is found that such behaviour conforms with little known facts within the current published – or even unpublished – records of the species. Two illustrative examples of significant, post-1936 sightings are presented and analysed below against the known body of scientific literature, none of them involving proof of the Thylacine's continued existence post 1936, but each of them, in its own way, profoundly interesting.

In 1952 Lindsay Crawford recorded a second-hand account of the successful post-1936 live snaring of a Thylacine in northern Tasmania. When approached by the snarers, the Thylacine made frantic efforts to escape, straining so hard to break the snare that each time it did so, haemorrhoids would be forced out of its anus. The observers described them as haemorrhoids, something they may well have had some familiarity with themselves. Now, for the time being, suspend disbelief. There is no known account of haemorrhoids in the Thylacine's scientific database, which, of course, does not mean that, if it was a snared Thylacine, that it could not have had haemorrhoids. But to the scientist, a more likely explanation is available. Thylacines were one of those rare marsupials in which both males as well as females possessed a pouch; the male pouch serving to protect the testes, which normally, were not on display. But the act of straining its body against the snare may well have forced the testes from the pouch, and to the non-specialist eye, their appearance at the base of the tail may well have suggested two haemorrhoids. For the record, the suggested date for this possible snaring was around 1940. While this account cannot possibly be considered proof of the continued existence of the Thylacine, from its internal evidence, measured against scientific knowledge, it is certainly a capture account of great interest.

In the early 1970s, in north-eastern Tasmania at Petal Point on Ringarooma Bay,

Russell Trickett (born in 1929), who had climbed to the top of a sand dune, saw a Thylacine walking away from him, heading inland "about half a mile away, then it dropped down into a gully, and I said its the last I see of that" (interview 31/8/2012). Rather than walking like a dog, it had "the gait of Welsh ponies" (interview 7/5/2013). There was a strong wind blowing from the west at the time. But shortly thereafter:

> It's coming towards me, and the damn thing up and sits as close as that window sill there [a distance of around 3 metres]. The mouth opens ... its top lip ... and hairs coming out ... twitching all the time. (interview 31/8/2012) The lips itself were turned out, there were patches of black on the lips. (interview 7/5/2013) This thing sat down. Now it sat on its tail, the tail came underneath it ... with its legs up in the front ... [the tail] seemed to have hair underneath it, but the main body was fur. The head went up and down like this [because] the neck was going up and down ... It was a female because of how it sat, with its pouch. (interview 31/8/2012) The pouch was open to be licked or cleaned. (interview 7/5/2013) But ... the wind circled around ... all of a sudden it must have got a whiff of me. (interview 31/8/2012) [It] broke into a yawn, then (interview 7/5//2013) it left in a hurry. (interview 31/8/2012)

Once again, let us suspend disbelief (and note that the following comments represent my interpretation, not that of Russell). Rather than a sighting of just one adult Thylacine, this potentially involves both members of a mated pair, with the male being the specimen seen walking away in the distance, and the female nearby. Russell noted the difference between the hairs on the tail and the fur on its belly, and when asked a key question as to whether it sat with a straight back like a dog, or a curved back like a cat, Russell answered correctly.[23] The female exhibited unusual behaviours, sitting on its tail, moving its head and neck up and down, with its lips unevenly raised over the teeth and in constant motion. The wind changed direction, the Thylacine became aware of Russell's presence, gave a threat yawn (as would be expected) and disappeared. Nobody ever witnessed or described the process of giving birth in a Thylacine, but from macropod parallels, one would certainly expect the female to sit with the tail beneath her. But once again, this is a sighting. It is not evidence for the continued existence of the Thylacine, nor may it be used to describe

---

[23]   A key diagnostic feature mentioned in the unpublished correspondence of Mary Roberts, founder of Beaumaris Zoo, Hobart.

the process of giving birth in Thylacines (which is my interpretation, not Russell's). That said, it has to be admitted that this sighting is interesting, very interesting. There is one further point of relevance worth making. The peak breeding season for the Thylacine took place in late winter/early spring (August/September), with the young probably born around four weeks later (Paddle, 2000). Russell recalled that his sighting took place 'in springtime" (interview 31/8/2012), later narrowing it down to "about October or November.' (interview 7/5/2013).

Records of Thylacines post 1936 are undoubtedly of interest - to the scientist as well as the lay researcher. While they do not amount to evidence for the continued existence of the species – once again, nothing but a body will change that designation – nevertheless, should that evidence be forthcoming, then the information obtained from recent sightings will be seen to possess valuable distributional and behavioural data of relevance to the continued welfare of the species. (As proved to be the case, in ornithological circles, with the rediscovery in 1990, after an absence of 78 years, of the night parrot, *Geopsittacus occidentalis*.) The reporting of modern Thylacine sightings is to be encouraged; and detailed records made of such incidents should be forwarded to either professional organisations, such as the Australian Rare Fauna Research Association, with its long history of existence and record keeping, and the social, legal and scientific expertise of its members; or to significant private individuals, such as Col Bailey, with a demonstrable public and private history in the handling of this information.

The designation of the extinction of the Thylacine is a working scientific hypothesis, and like all scientific hypotheses, it is one capable of being disproved. Such disproof would be welcomed by scientists. To return to T.H. Huxley, remember that the next 'best of all things is to be clearly and definitely wrong'. All power to those associations and individuals who may achieve this.

Acknowledgements

The perspective presented here on recent Thylacine sightings arose from many fruitful discussions, first with the sadly departed Phil Andrews, Peter Chapple, Eric Guiler and Heinz Moeller; and secondly from contemporary source input from Nick Mooney, Lindsay Crawford, Mike Cleeland, Lothar Frenz, Rex Hesline, Lyne Selwood, Stephen Sleightholme, Chris Tracy and Dorothy Williams. Thanks to my student, Victoria Devine, for introducing me to her grandfather, Russell Trickett (and obviously thanks to Russell as well). Joan Dixon and Kathryn Medlock read drafts of this chapter and their constructive comments were most valuable.

~~~

*Dr Robert Paddle is an animal behaviourist at Australian Catholic University and commentator on the history and philosophy of science. He is also the author of the critically acclaimed **The Last Tasmanian Tiger**, which received the Whitley Medal of the Zoological Society of New South Wales for best science book of 2001.*

References

Akerman, K. and Willing, T. (2009). An ancient rock painting of a marsupial lion, *Thylacoleo carnifex*, from the Kimberley, Western Australia. *Antiquity*, **83** (319).

Barrett, C. (1944) *Isle of Mountains. Roaming through Tasmania.* Melbourne: Cassell.

Crawford, L.D. (1958). The Tasmanian tiger and its relatives. *Skyline*, (4), 12-14.

Darwin, C.R. (1859). *On the Origin of Species.* London: Murray.

Field Naturalist's Society of the Royal Society of South Australia. (1888). *The Problem of Our Native Fauna and Flora.* Adelaide: Author.

Flannery, T. (2012) After the future: Australia's new extinction crisis. *Quarterly Essay*, (49), 1-80.

Flannery, T. and Schouten, P. (2001). *A Gap in Nature: Discovering the world's extinct animals.* Melbourne: Text Publishing.

Freeman, C. (2010). *Paper Tiger: A visual history of the Thylacine.* Leiden, The Netherlands: Brill.

Gould, J. (1851). *The Mammals of Australia. Volume 1, Part iii.* London: Taylor and Francis.

Guiler, E.R. (1985). *Thylacine: The Tragedy of the Tasmanian Tiger.* Melbourne: Oxford University Press.

Gunn, R.C. (1836). Letter to Sir William Hooker, 26/11/1836. In Burns, T.E. and Skemp, J.R. (eds) *Van Diemen's Land Correspondents,* (1961). Launceston: Queen Victoria Museum.

Gunn, R.C. (1837). Letter to Sir William Hooker, 31/3/1837. In Burns, T.E. and Skemp,

J.R. (eds) *Van Diemen's Land Correspondents,* (1961). Launceston: Queen Victoria Museum.

Gunn, R.C. (1850). *Zoology (draft manuscript).* R.C. Gunn Correspondence, MLA 258, Mitchell Library, State Library of New South Wales.

Gunn, R.C. (1852). Zoology. In West, J. (ed) *The History of Tasmania. With copious information respecting the colonies of New South Wales, Victoria, South Australia, etc, etc, etc.* Launceston: Henry Dowling.

Harris, G.P. (1808). Description of two new species of *Didelphis* from Van Diemen's Land.*Transactions of the Linnaean Society of London, 9,* 174-178.

Healy, T. and Cropper, P. (1994). *Out of the Shadows: Mystery Animals of Australia.*Sydney: Ironbark Press.

Jenkins, C.F.H. (1977) *The Noah's Ark Syndrome. (One hundred years of acclimatization and zoo development in Australia.).* Perth: Zoological Gardens Board.

Le Souëf, A.S. and Burrell, H. (1926) *The Wild Animals of Australasia: Embracing the mammals of New Guinea and the nearer Pacific Islands. With a chapter on the bats of Australia and New Guinea by Ellis Le G. Troughton.* London: George Harrup.

Le Souëf, W.H.D. (1907) *Wild Life in Australia.* Melbourne: Whitcombe and Tombs.

Owen, R. (1842) Account of a *Thylacinus,* the great dog-headed opossum, one of the rarest and largest of the Marsupiate family of animals. *Report of the Eleventh Meeting of the British Association for the Advancement of Science; held at Plymouth in July 1841.* London: John Murray.

Owen, R. (1843) On the rudimental marsupial bones in the *Thylacinus. Proceedings of the Zoological Society of London,* 148-149.

Paddle, R.N. (2000) *The Last Tasmanian Tiger. The History and Extinction of the Thylacine.* Cambridge: Cambridge University Press.

Paddle, R.N. (2002) Book Review: A Gap in Nature. Discovering the world's extinct animals. *Australian Zoologist,* **32**(1), 174-175.

Paddle, R.N. (2012) The thylacine's last straw: epidemic disease in a recent mammalian extinction. *Australian Zoologist,* **36** (1), 75-92.

Routh, J.E. (1902) Huxley as a literary man. *The Century Illustrated Monthly Magazine,* January,**63** (3), 392-398.

Secretary, Animals and Birds Protection Board. (1938) *Letter to the Society for the Preservation of the Fauna of the Empire, 25/3/1938.* Animals and Birds Protection Board Correspondence, 1928 – 1948, AA 612/35. Archives Office of Tasmania.

Sheridan, B.G. (1871) Letter to P.L. Sclater. *Proceedings of the Zoological Society of London,* 629-630.

Troughton, E. (1941) *Furred Animals of Australia,* (first edition). Sydney: Angus and Robertson.

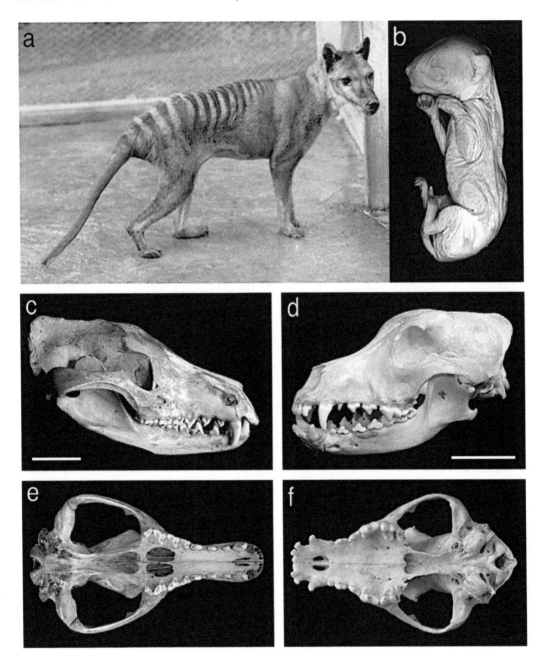

Figure 1. The Thylacine, Thylacinus cynocephalus. (a) Young male Thylacine in Hobart Zoo in 1928. (b) A preserved pouch young specimen (head length 34 mm) from the Museum Victoria collection. (c-f) The skull of the Thylacine (c, e) compared with that of the domestic dog Canis canis (d, f). The morphology of the skull shows remarkable convergent evolution compared to a dog. Scale bar = 5cm.
Courtesy Andrew Pask et al., 2009.

CHAPTER 10

Thinking Beyond Extinction
by Dr Andrew Pask

While science is not yet at the level of being able to bring an extinct species back to life, we can gain access to their genetic code or genome. The genome contains the animal's complete genetic code, providing critical insights into the biology of an extinct species. The less time it has been since the extinction event, the more intact the DNA is. Recent estimates indicate that DNA is no longer viable after around 1.5 million years, making DNA harvest impossible for most ancient extinct species such as dinosaurs for example. However, for recently extinct species such as the Thylacine, sequencing the entire genome is a real possibility.

This is particularly feasible in the case of the Thylacine since so many specimens have been well preserved in museum collections across the globe. Portions of the Thylacine genome have already been recovered and even had their function resurrected in developing mice embryos. This work has revealed new information on the biology of this unique and enigmatic marsupial, as well as providing insights into its ecology before and during its demise. This chapter will explore the value in sequencing the Thylacine genome and what it means for the potential future of this species.

Genome sequencing

Several types of Thylacine tissues can be found in museum collections ranging from bones to whole fixed pouch young (Thylacine pups) and tanned pelts or skins. DNA has been extracted from each of these types of samples and was highly fragmented with a size range from 50-400bp with the peak size averaging approximately 130bp. However, in contrast to working with DNA from more ancient samples such as the Neanderthal or mammoth, the fragmented DNA is at least highly abundant.

In the past, the small size of the DNA fragments posed a major impediment to sequencing the genome. But now, the DNA fragment size range is perfectly suited to the new next generation sequencing platforms that are capable of sequencing complete genomes in just a few hours.

Sequencing is just one hurdle; the next challenging part is putting the tiny pieces back together. The marsupial genome is just a bit smaller than ours, weighing in at around 3 billion bases (or individual letters). Now, if you think of the Thylacine genome randomly broken up into 100 base sections, that means, at a minimum, you are looking at a 30 million-piece puzzle. But because of DNA damage and the way the DNA is randomly broken up you need at least 20 times that many to start building a decent draft genome.

Further complicating the genome puzzle is the fact that around 50 per cent of mammalian genomes are made up of repeated sequences. If we think of this as an analogy to a puzzle, its like trying to put together at 30 million piece puzzle for which you have over 300 million pieces, and 50 per cent of those are just blue sky (i.e. they look the same) making it very hard to figure out who connects with who. On top of that, we don't know exactly what to expect in terms of the final outcome – so we are essentially doing the puzzle without any picture on the box to guide us.

Fortunately, the genomes of a few other marsupials have been sequenced, including the Tasmanian devil, Tammar wallaby and North American opossum. Together these genomes provide a very good guide for us in deciphering which parts of the Thylacine puzzle go where. Even so, there will always be large sections of the Thylacine genome, which are dense in repeats that will never be fully deciphered and are not deciphered yet for even living species with completely intact genomes. Equally important as the development of new machines that can perform genome sequencing on this scale, has been the development of supercomputers and sophisticated algorithms to perform these genome assemblies from all the tiny pieces. Using a combination of different tissue types and methods we have recovered a large portion of the Thylacine genome already and the complete sequence of it mitochondrial DNA (see below; *Thylacine Diversity*).

Another complication of working with old and ancient DNA is that it accrues damage over time. Letters in the genetic code can become distorted or lost altogether. This has been a major hurdle for the Neanderthal and mammoth genome assemblies (putting the puzzle together) as now some parts may not fit together exactly as expected, but still form part of a continuous sequence. The good news for the Thylacine is that damage to their DNA is minimal (<0.6 per cent). In addition, several recent advances in ancient DNA technology have also improved the quality of sequencing from damaged DNA samples by pretreating with repair enzyme cocktails.

These proteins can scan the Thylacine DNA and fix broken bases allowing them to be sequenced more efficiently.

Defining the complete Thylacine genome (or at least the part which is unique and not repetitive) will create an invaluable resource for the research community and provide a vast array of information on the genetics and biology of this incredibly unique extinct species. The sequence will also expand the limited list of marsupial genomes that are proving to be very valuable resources for genetics, biology and biomedicine. One example of this is the antimicrobial genes that were recently isolated from the Tammar wallaby genome. These genes have the potential to produce therapeutic drugs that can kill many of the antibiotic resistant bacteria, which cause major problems in hospitals across the globe. Marsupials have a lot of these sorts of genes in their genome as the very small young at birth do not have an immune system yet and must be protected from infection by these genes while developing in the pouch.

Thylacine Diversity

Genetic diversity refers to the amount of differences that exist in the genomes of different individuals. Importantly, genetic diversity is directly correlated with the health of a species. Species that have a large amount of variation among individuals in the population are much more able to adapt to changing environments such as pressures from disease causing agents. This is because the variation inherent in the population makes it more likely that some individuals may have gene variations that can overcome this pressure. Conversely, if a population has very limited diversity, once a disease takes hold, it can quickly spread from individual to individual. A classic example of this is the facial tumor disease currently sweeping through the Tasmanian devil population and posing the threat of extinction. Tasmanian devils have extremely low genetic diversity so the disease can jump easily from animal to animal. Currently, the only way to combat this aggressive disease is to prevent animals from exposure to the virus by isolation. So if the Tasmanian devil does manage to survive this disease outbreak, it means that the remaining population will need to be closely monitored and managed if we are to ensure its long-term survival.

As mentioned above, one of the first outcomes of sequencing the Thylacine genome was the complete sequence of its mitochondrial genome. The mitochondria are small energy producing factories within our cells. Each of these factories has a mini genome of its own of around 17 thousand bases. Each cell has 100-10,000 copies of this genome, making it much more abundant than the rest of the DNA and quite easy to sequence from even very degraded samples. The mitochondrial genome is also very stable and acquires mutations, or changes to the genetic code, at a very predictable rate. For this reason, the mitochondrial genome can be used to assess the how much genetic diversity exists within a species. Another key feature of the mitochondrial genome is that it is only inherited from your mother and so it can also be used to trace your maternal lineage.

Once the complete Thylacine mitochondrial genome was determined, it makes it relatively simple to sample that same sequence from other specimens using a technique called the polymerase chain reaction or PCR. PCR was used to examine the mitochondrial DNA of 12 Thylacines collected between 1852 and 1909. The bounty placed on Thylacines started in 1888, so this range of specimens includes some collected before their major decline.

The analyses showed that diversity in the Thylacine is even lower than that seen in the Tasmanian devil. This suggests that the Thylacine was in very poor genetic health in spite of it being hunted to extinction.

Genetic diversity accumulates in a population over many generations but can be quickly lost if a large number of animals in the population die or a few animals become reproductively isolated. The latter is what is hypothesised to have occurred in the Thylacine.

Tasmania was once connected to mainland Australia by a land bridge. During this time, several marsupial species such as the Thylacine migrated from the mainland to Tasmania. The extremely limited variation in the Thylacine's genome would suggest just a few individuals founded this Tasmanian population which ultimately become the only surviving population. A similar fate presumably led to the limited diversity in the Tasmanian devil also. This limited genetic diversity poses a further impediment (beyond the current technical deficiencies) to bringing this, or indeed any extinct species back to life (see below; *Species Resurrection*).

Convergent evolution

One of the most fascinating features of the Thylacine is its body design. The Thylacine looks almost exactly like a dog from the structure of its limbs, to its skull and even its teeth (Figure 1). However, dogs belong to a group of mammals called eutherians while the Thylacine was a marsupial. Marsupials and eutherians are two very distantly related mammalian lineages that last shared a common ancestor around 160 million years ago (Figure 2).

Furthermore, the common ancestor that eventually evolved into the Thylacine and dog was much more rat-like than dog-like. This means that the Thylacine and the dog independently evolved a very similar body plan, likely due to their similar mode of life as nomadic hunters. When two different species independently arrive, or converge, at the same body design, this is described as convergent evolution. A classic example of convergent evolution is wing formation in the bird and the bat, which are very distantly related but both evolved forelimbs specialized for flight. Of all the examples of convergent evolution in mammals, none approach the level of convergence seen between the Thylacine and the dog.

In terms of evolution comparing the genomes of the Thylacine and dog will provide insight into how each species arrived at the same body plan. It is commonly thought that our genomes contain a limited set of tools that can be utilised to modify body form. If this is true, then we might expect to find that both dogs and marsupials have utilized these tools in similar ways to arrive at their body plan. If this is not the case, then we might expect to find a host of changes unique to each species, which have driven their development. The Thylacine and dog comparison is ideal for investigating this question because marsupials and eutherian mammals have been evolving independently of each other for around 160 million years. This divergence time is sufficiently close that important and functional regions of the genome look very similar between marsupial and eutherian genomes, but sufficiently distant that any non-functional regions of the genome no longer share any similarity.

Comparing the genomes of marsupial and eutherian species has been fundamental in unraveling the complexities of the mammalian genome and has enabled the identification of key genes and promoters of genes that regulate development of the body plan. The Thylacine genome can be used in the same way to answer questions on the genes and mechanisms used to change the body design in evolving mammals.

Gene resurrection

Sequencing the genome is one way to gain insight into the biology of the Thylacine but it is not without its limitations. We can infer a lot about gene function by looking at how it has changed in sequence and evolved over time, but this inference lacks tangible proof that such sequence changes may have altered gene function. In order to determine how changes might have changed the function of a gene it is necessary to resurrect its function in a living system. A gene from the Thylacine was the first ever piece of extinct DNA to be functionally resurrected in another entire living organism, the mouse. The mouse was used for such experiments, as it is the best-developed mammal model for performing the necessary genetic manipulations. That is inserting a piece of Thylacine DNA into every living cell within the organism through a process called transgenesis.

In order for the piece of ancient DNA to functional normally within its host organism it must retain the ability to bond the same proteins and factors that it did in the ordinal species. To put that more simply, the mouse needs to have all the same factors to switch the gene on that existed in the Thylacine or the Thylacine DNA will not be able to be activated and we wont be able to study its function. Fortunately, these switch genes and the sequences to which they bind in the genome are very highly conserved and work very well even between species separated for 160 million years and even more.

Initial experiments in the Thylacine involved the isolation of a segment of a gene (*Col2A1*) that is important for early development of the mammalian skeleton. This particular sequence, known as an enhancer region, is important for telling the gene when and where to be switched on in the embryo during development. This can then be placed into a mouse and we can see how the Thylacine gene might have functioned. In order to visualize when and where this gene is activated during embryonic development, the Thylacine DNA was coupled with a reporter gene. This reporter gene (LacZ) will stain cells blue when the Thylacine DNA is turned on. The result of this experiment was the discovery that the Thylacine*Col2A1* enhancer expression matched almost exactly that of the mouse *Col2a1* gene during development (Figure 3). This tells us that this gene is not likely to have changed much in function between these two species.

Furthermore, we can determine that the associated factors required to induce expression from this promoter have remained sufficiently conserved between mice and marsupials despite 160 million years of divergent evolution between these species. In the future, such experiments can be used to determine the altered expression domains of genes that may have undergone convergent evolution. This technique of gene resurrection that was devised using the Thylacine has much broader applicability to any extinct species for which DNA can be obtained. Using this method it is now possible to go beyond the genome sequence to actually examine functionality of extinct genes.

Species Resurrection

One of the most commonly asked questions of scientists working on ancient DNA is can we use this information to bring these species back to life? Currently the answer to this question is no.

Sequencing a genome is an entirely different experiment to trying to use this information to make a living organism. As discussed above, even the most intensively sequenced genomes, such as the mouse and human, are still missing large regions. These regions include the centromere (a region of the chromosome that is essential for their correct segregation when the cells divide), the telomeres (the ends of chromosomes), the Y chromosome (essential for male sexual development and spermatogenesis) as well as many other regions dense with repeat sequences. All of these regions are essential to species viability.

It is likely that due to the fragmentation of old and ancient DNA specimens such as the Thylacine, that such regions will never be able to be defined. Even if they could be, we currently lack the technology to turn our short genome reads into a complete functioning chromosome within a living cell. But all is not lost.

The most likely scenario for resurrecting an extinct animal would be to tinker with the genome of a closely related species that is extant (currently living) and from which stable cell lines can be derived. For example, cells could be established from the elephant and using recombinant DNA techniques, it could be made to look mammoth like by switching out regions of DNA where the two species differ. This is never going to be 100 per cent mammoth, but might end up being very close.

In the case of the Thylacine, one might use Tasmanian devil or numbat to act as the host genome to tinker with dependent on which one would require the least amount of changes to look Thylacine-like. The technologies for switching out parts of the genetic code for another do exist, as well as then taking this cell and using it to derive a living organism.

However, at the moment this is only done on a very small scale, switching out a small region or two at a time. The types of changes required to make a numbat genome resemble a Thylacine could number in the millions and is still currently beyond the scope of what is feasible in the research lab.

Even if researchers were to create a 'Thylacine-like' genome, we still lack the reproductive techniques in marsupials to turn this cell into a living organism. Such experiments require a recipient mother that can have their reproductive cycle controlled and manipulated to firstly provide unfertilized eggs for transplantation of the Thylacine-like cell nucleus and then so it can be returned to a uterus that thinks it is going into a pregnancy. Such methods are not yet well established for even broadly used marsupial species.

Right now, continuing to mine the Thylacine genome is perhaps our best bet to gaining insight in the biology and ecology of this amazingly unique marsupial and is the most tangible approach to preserving as much of the legacy of this species as possible. Such studies may eventually help to pave the way for future resurrection efforts should technologies ever improve.

~~~

Dr Andrew Pask is Associate Professor, Genetics and Genomics at the University of Connecticut. Dr Pask was part of a team from the University of Melbourne that made history in 2008 when they successfully inserted part of a Thylacine gene involved in bone growth into mice, and confirmed that it functioned.

RECOMMENDED FURTHER READING

Books and Articles

Bailey, C. (2001) Tiger Tales: Stories of the Tasmanian Tiger. HarperCollins. ISBN 0732269253

Bailey, C. (2013) Shadow of the Thylacine. Five Mile Press. ISBN 9781743464854

Guiler, E. (1985) Thylacine: The Tragedy of the Tasmanian Tiger. Oxford University Press. ISBN 9780195546033

Guiler, E. & Godard, P. (1998) Tasmanian Tiger: A Lesson to be Learnt. Abrolhos Publishing. ISBN 9780958579100

Guiler, E. R. (1961a). Breeding Season of the Thylacine. Journal of Mammalogy 42 (3): 396–397. JSTOR 1377040

Guiler, E. R. (1961b) The Former Distribution and Decline of the Thylacine. Australian Journal of Science 23(7): 207–210.

Healy T. & Cropper, P. (1994) Out of the Shadows: Mystery Animals of Australia. Ironbark Press. ISBN 0330274996

Lord, C. (1927). Existing Tasmanian marsupials. Papers and Proceedings of the Royal Society of Tasmania 61: 17–24.

Lowry, D. C. (1967) Discovery of a Thylacine (Tasmanian Tiger) Carcass in a Cave near Eucla, Western Australia. Helictite.

Mittelbach, M. & Crewdson, M. (2005) Carnivorous Nights: On the Trail of the Tasmanian Tiger. Random House. ISBN 1400060028

Owen, David (2003). Thylacine: The Tragic Tale of the Tasmanian Tiger. Allen & Unwin. ISBN 9781865087580

Paddle, Robert. (2000) The Last Tasmanian Tiger: The History and Extinction of the Thylacine. Cambridge University Press. ISBN 9780521531542

Park, A. (1986) Tasmanian Tiger: Extinct or Merely Elusive? Australian Geographic. Vol. 1 No 3, July-Sept 1986.

Pearce, R. (1976) Thylacines in Tasmania. Australian Mammal Society Bulletin **3**: 58.

Slee, S. (1987) The Haunt of the Marsupial Wolf. South West Printing and Publishing Company, Bunbury WA.

Sleightholme, S. & Ayliffe, N. (2005) International Thylacine Specimen Database. CD-Rom. Master Copy: Zoological Society, London

Smith, M. (1996) Bunyips and Bigfoots. Millennium Books. ISBN 9781864290813

Smith, S. J. (1980) The Tasmanian Tiger – 1980. A report on an investigation of the current status of thylacine Thylacinus cynocephalus, funded by the World Wildlife Fund Australia. Hobart: National Parks and Wildlife Service, Tasmania.

Terry, N. (2005) Tasmanian Tiger Thylacinus cynocephalus: Alive and Well. ISBN 0975764802

Wallace, L. (2004) Hold That Tiger. A Robyn's Nest Production.

Williams, M & Lang, R. (2010) Australian Big Cats: An Unnatural History of Panthers. Strange Nation Publishing. ISBN 9780646530079

Websites

CFZ Australia - **www.cfzaustralia.com**

The Search for the Tasmanian Tiger - **www.australian-tasmanian-tiger.com**

The Thylacine Museum - **www.naturalworlds.org/thylacine/index.htm**

Buck and Joan Emberg's Tasmanian-Tiger.com -**www.tasmanian-tiger.com**

Australian Rare Fauna Research Association – **www.arfra.org**

T.R.U. - **www.thylacineresearchunit.org**

Have you seen a Tasmanian Tiger?

Report sightings and information to Mike Williams on 0416 303 371 or email **mike@asecretcountry.com**

MORE TITLES FROM

STRANGE NATION PUBLISHING

WWW.STRANGENATION.COM.AU

It's Australia's greatest wildlife mystery – are there really 'big cats' roaming the bush?

Sightings of large black panthers have been occurring in Australia for the past 150 years, leading to speculation there may be a breeding colony of these large cats in Australia.

These large cats – predominantly black, but also tan in colour – have only afforded their witnesses fleeting glimpses, and left behind tantalising clues: scraps of fur, a paw print or three, unusually large scats, and livestock carcasses surgically dismembered and picked clean of flesh.

In their wake, they leave carnage and bewilderment: What are they? How did they get here? The authors don't just ask the questions, they seek the answers, and what they have found will intrigue the sceptic and the believer alike.

Australia isn't the only antipodean country touched by the black cat mystery. **Australian Big Cats: An Unnatural History of Panthers** also dedicates a chapter to the profusion of sightings and speculation in neighbouring New Zealand, documenting reports right up until 2009 and sharing for the first time highlights from the unpublished manuscript of New Zealand's first big cat hunter.

Flesh-and-blood or flight of fancy? Exotic pest, mutant feral or 'extinct' marsupial lion? Join authors Michael Williams and Rebecca Lang as they explore one of Australia's weirdest animal mysteries.

Read more at **www.australianbigcats.com**.

AUSTRALIAN BIG CATS

An Unnatural History of PANTHERS

Michael Williams & Rebecca Lang

A gripping mystery from the heart of 'Cougar Country', Cordering, Western Australia

In the late 1970s, journalist David O'Reilly stumbled across a mystery bigger than the state of Western Australia itself - wildcats the size of dogs attacking farm livestock!

These cats resembled North American mountain lions - also know as pumas, cougars or catamounts - and terrorised the district of Cordering with their presence.

David wrote a series of newspaper articles about the attacks, and sightings of the large cats, in *The Australian* newspaper. What followed was a bizarre sequence of events that would alienate farmers, generate a government inquiry and draw claims of a conspiracy to keep the truth silent.

A couple of years after the strange events David put it all together in a book - this book, **Savage Shadow: The Search for the Australian Cougar** - which would go on to gain status as an Australian cult classic.

With few copies available and the story highly sought after even today, a decision was made in conjunction with the O'Reilly family to re-print the book via Strange Nation Publishing.

What was really going on in Cordering in the late 1970s? You'll have to read it to believe it.

Read more at **www.australianbigcats.com**.

"A CLASSIC, TIMELESS WORK BACK IN PRINT AT LAST." DR KARL SHUKER

SAVAGE SHADOW

The Search for the Australian Cougar

David O'Reilly

FOREWORD BY MICHAEL WILLIAMS & REBECCA LANG

A Tasmanian devil in captivity. *Courtesy of Rebecca Lang.*

Some of the proceeds from this book
will be donated to conservation efforts
protecting the Tasmanian Devil.
Thank you for helping to make
a difference.